LC 8/2016

To Steer by the Stars

To Steer by the Stars

THE STORY OF
NATHANIEL BOWDITCH

☆

PAUL RINK

DOUBLEDAY & COMPANY, INC., GARDEN CITY, NEW YORK

Acknowledgment is made to the American Heritage Publishing Company for their kind permission to use material published in the Volume XI, Number 5, August 1960 edition of *American Heritage*.

Endpapers and frontispiece courtesy of Peabody Museum of Salem

Preface

When the first caveman paddled his dugout canoe away from the cove or inlet or river mouth where he made his home, and the land faded into the mists behind him, he was immediately faced with two problems which were completely new in his experience. What direction should he guide his craft to get to where he wanted to go? And what direction should he steer to get him back home again? It was as simple, and complicated, as that!

Once this early, intrepid voyager was out of sight of familiar landmarks—a hill, a tree, a jutting rock—the changeless surface of the ocean and the vast, empty arc of the sky offered no clues to his landbound eyes. Men are restless creatures though, and even these early sailors looked to far horizons. As soon as the art of making reasonably safe ships had developed, they began to seek

[3]

distant lands. The stories that ancient mariners never ventured out of sight of land are old wives' tales. In every civilization, adventurous seamen made long, long voyages. The earliest ones were in that land-locked sea, the Mediterranean, when early sailors traded between Africa, Greece, and what is now the coast of Spain and France. The first sailors to venture through the Straits of Gibraltar, or the Gates of Hercules as they called it, were the Phoenicians. They are known to have voyaged as far as Britain after tin in the mines of Cornwall, by 600 B.C. So it was that very, very early, sailors had to begin the art of navigation. It is one of man's oldest sciences.

As the first venturesome mariners worked their tossing cockleshells along the coasts, and then finally far out of sight of land, they began to realize that the sea and the sky were not trackless wastes. To the observant, there were guideposts. Slowly information began to accumulate. Seaman's feel, seaman's horse sense developed and this lore was passed on at first by word of mouth, from pilot to pilot, from father to son. At last it was put down in old manuscripts, books, charts.

For example, three thousand years before the discovery of the compass (the *needle* it was called, because the earliest compasses consisted of a magnetized needle floating on a bit of cork or chip of wood) it was observed that in certain places the winds always came from the same direction and could be relied upon to blow a ship safely to her destination. Out of this was born the idea of North and South. And from the sun, which rose always in one place and soared across the heavens to set in another, arose the idea of East and West. Also, mariners noticed that certain blazing stars never seemed to move, but remained fixed, hanging in the sky in a location that did not change. So it was that out of such natural heavenly phenomena, the idea of direction developed. The four positions, the four great cardinal points were laid out.

Slowly, over the centuries, knowledge accumulated to help the sailor. The sea itself provided clues and tools to tell him where he was, and how he should steer. Currents, birds, floating bits of seaweed, the shape of clouds, gave answers to those who knew how to use them. Even the bottom of the sea helped. Near land a heavy weight on a line recorded depth. When a smear of tallow on the bottom of the weight touched bottom, it brought up samples of mud, of sand, of shells, all of which was valuable information to the man with experience.

Methods of determining the speed of a ship were invented. If a captain knew for example, how far his vessel had gone along a certain course, it was very helpful. The earliest determination of speed was made by dropping a small piece of wood from the bow and timing its passage to the stern. This was long before the advent of clocks, so this timing was done with a small sandglass, or even by a man counting the beats of his heart. From this early "chip" of wood comes the modern term of "log." Later methods involved dropping a drag on a line over the stern and then checking how much of the line ran out in a given period of time as the ship moved through the water. The line had knots tied in it at regular intervals to indicate distance, and hence today the word "knots" is still used to indicate the speed of a ship.

So it was that slowly and painstakingly, and with much loss of life and of ships, the science of navigation developed. It was pretty well hit-and-miss for a long time, however. The best it could do was to give the mariner a rough idea of where he was or how far he had come. There was no such thing as precision navigation. Then a wonderful thing happened. Instruments were invented to point direction accurately and to measure accurately the stars and their paths.

The first was the compass. Nobody knows who the early genius was who invented it, or when he lived, but surely the discovery that a piece of lodestone (a bit of naturally magnetized iron ore) would always point to the north if it could move easily, as for example if it were floated on a chip in a bowl of water, is among man's greatest discoveries. It is said that the compass was a Chinese invention and that, oddly enough, at first it had nothing to do with the sea. The first compasses were used to guide caravans and armies across the empty wastes of Asia, which in their own way presented just as difficult a problem for the "navigator" as the oceans did for the sailor.

The first known use of a compass at sea was relatively recent. It was in A.D. 1180, when an English sailor placed a bit of lodestone on a small wooden dart and floated it. When the constellation of the Bear, which he had been using to guide himself northward to home, was hidden by clouds, he simply continued on his course by aiming the bow of his ship in the direction the point of his dart indicated.

Slowly also the science of astronomy began to find solutions to the task of the navigator. From the time of the earliest Greeks, astronomers had been studying the heavens. They noticed that some stars moved and others didn't. One of those that was fixed blazed night after night far

[6]

in the North. They gave it the name of Polaris, the Pole Star, because it hung like a glowing beacon over the North Pole.

They observed that the height of this star in the sky changed as the observer changed his position on the earth. At the Equator, Polaris seemed right on the horizon. And, they reasoned, if a man could stand on the North Pole, the star would be directly overhead, at an angle of 90 degrees to the horizon. They were quite right.

The farther north a man went from the Equator, the higher Polaris seemed to be. If for example, he saw that Polaris was halfway between the horizon and directly overhead, that is at an angle of 45 degrees, he knew that *he* was at a point halfway between the Equator and the North Pole. If Polaris was a third of the way up, then the observer was a third of the way to the Pole from the Equator. Out of this idea came the concept of *latitude*— positions and distances north or south of the Equator. These early astronomers drew lines around the earth parallel to the Equator and thus divided the globe into *degrees, or parallels of latitude.*

The idea was extremely simple, and brilliant. It wasn't much good for mariners, though, to determine *exact* positions in a north-south direction until proper instruments had been invented which could measure accurately the height, or altitude, of Polaris and other such stars.

Centuries were to go by before such instruments had been developed and, in the meantime, many strange and cumbersome devices were used. Then in 1731 an Englishman named John Hadley perfected what he called a *quadrant.* An American, a glassmaker and experimenter in optics named Thomas Godfrey invented a similar quadrant in Philadelphia about the same time. Very shortly, refinements were made in the quadrant, and it became the *sextant,* still in use today.

In southern latitudes, that is, in positions on our globe which lie between the Equator and the South Pole, the problem was more difficult. The South Pole has no convenient fixed star like Polaris hanging directly over it. The problem was solved in other ways, and eventually mariners had various methods available to them. They could choose whichever was most convenient—methods using Polaris, other fixed stars such as Sirius or Vega, or even from calculations involving the altitude of the sun exactly at noontime.

Thus it was that not only Polaris, but a whole galaxy of stars became useful to the navigator. So important did the heavens become to the navigator that accurate maps were made of the skies, showing the paths and the predicted positions of all of them that were important. The most famous of all these maps was published in England in 1722. It was called the *Great Star Catalogue* and was of inestimable help to mariners everywhere.

And so it was that bit by bit the science of navigation developed over the centuries. Nevertheless, even as late as 1800 those who ventured forth on the sea in ships had very little idea exactly where they were. When familiar landmarks faded into the mists astern, navigators were pretty well lost; to make matters even worse, they could only guess roughly at the location of the port to which they were bound.

Vessels wandered over the oceans in great sweeps, in circles and zigzags. People often lost their lives, their ships

[8]

and their cargoes simply because no one knew how to determine positions precisely on the surface of our globe.

Today, the contrails of a big jet can point a straight and true path in the sky, an ocean liner can cross the sea in a matter of days, or a rocket can streak directly for the moon. All of these things are possible, partly because of the work of a frail little man who lived long ago in Salem, Massachusetts. What he did and thought, and insisted upon in the face of ridicule and tradition, helps us find our way about the earth and through the heavens without becoming lost or wasting time.

P.R.

To Steer by the Stars

One

☆

On a golden misty spring afternoon long ago a young boy
ran down a hill as fast as he could toward the docks of a
small town in Massachusetts. Soft sea wind blew to him
from over the harbor. It brought to his nostrils the scent
of the ocean and to his ears the mewing of gulls and the
steady wash of the bay on the shoreline.

He was twelve, thirteen, maybe fourteen years of age.
To tell the truth, he was so small and scrawny that it
would have been hard to make any close guess. The only
thing that might have helped was the size of his head.
It was very large, too large for his body, with a high,
domed forehead swelling out over eyes which looked upon
the world with a maturity far beyond that suggested by
the rest of his appearance.

He reached the village. The whole town streamed

through the streets with him. Pale clerks from the counting houses, swarthy, singing seamen from the taverns, dignified ship chandlers, merchants from the shops—men, women, children, old people—everyone in town poured from the buildings and houses and headed for Derby pier.

On a street corner with a clear view of the harbor, the boy paused. He gazed out over the water. There she was!

Under the press of a gentle afternoon breeze, a big square-rigged ship ghosted slowly toward the land. In spite of his determination not to miss a moment of her arrival, the boy stood frozen still a moment, utterly spellbound by the beautiful sight.

The ship was framed against the light blue sky and the green hills and the rooftops of the tiny hamlet of Beverly across the bay. She had a fresh, shining, bright look, as though the months and months at sea under the rains, the winds, and the suns of every latitude had scrubbed her clean of all traces of the dirt of the land. Her sails were bleached white and shining, and they towered like a swaying pillar of clouds above her hull, reaching for the sky. To the small boy this vessel seemed the loveliest thing on earth. Compared to the majestic, blue-water ship, the grimy work schooners, the brigs, the brigantines, and all the other small craft in the harbor were ugly mud birds.

He gazed at her, entranced. Without realizing it, he took in every detail of her appearance. Her masts, spars, the delicate and complex tracery of her rigging—these and much more flashed before his eyes and left their impression on his mind. The ship seemed dainty, fragile, and poised, and yet he knew this was only an illusion. He knew that every stick, every line, every shroud and spar was tense, taut as a violin string, ready for instant re-

[14]

action. The bitter world of the rolling sea was the home of this ship; it was a hard and savage world where destruction waited always to punish the first weakness.

In addition to the physical appearance of the ship, other things also registered on the boy. This voyage had been a long one in dangerous waters. How were the people in her? Had anyone died, or been lost? Would there be saddened homes in the town tonight? She was very deeply laden, so probably the voyage had been a successful and profitable one. How would this affect the town and its people? All this, and more, passed through the boy's mind as he stood gazing over the harbor.

This was the seaport of Salem, Massachusetts, in the year 1785. The safe homecoming of a big Indiaman, two years out, was an event which touched the whole town to its heart.

Salem was a one-way-of-life town. There was only the sea to give it life. It was the gateway to the whole wide world and it existed only because of the sea. The beautiful ships and the tough mariners who sailed them down the channel to the far oceans of the earth were the final expression of all the work and hopes and dreams of the port and its people.

Any Salem boy felt all this, because the sea had influenced his life from the very moment of his birth. The smells of the ocean and of the spume and drying kelp along the beaches and the sea wrack on the rocks were among his earliest impressions. At nights he drifted off to sleep with the pounding of the waves and the scary tolling of the bell buoys in his ears. His young eyes very early learned the importance of the seasons, and the positions of the sun and stars and the moon, as well as the yellow glimmer of the beacon on Baker Light, because these were all among the things which helped guide Salem ships safely home.

And while he was still very small, he learned the meaning of fear when he heard the great winter storms thundering and boiling down out of the north. When a Salem ship was long, long overdue, he also felt that fear. In the little church he said the words of old prayers along with the wives and children and sweethearts of the men who had sailed in her, and of the shipowners who had entrusted their fortunes to her.

Later, as he played along the rocks and beaches and docks, he learned how to swim and row and sail a boat. He listened wide-eyed to the tales the old graybeards spun about ships and deep water, about Cape Horn, about the majestic seabirds and the ghosts of drowned sailors. Also, he paid very special attention as they taught him to tie knots for every purpose—knots that would hold tight and strong and never fail and yet would always come loose in a hurry with just the right twist on the right spot.

When he was older and started exploring the shipyards, he saw how the ships were put together. He observed the rigging, the rake of the masts, the splendid curve of the bow, and the sweet stretch of the hull falling away amidships and then rising again toward the stern. He learned to estimate whether a ship might be handy, easy to manage, obedient, and willing, or whether perhaps she might be cranky and difficult or even a man-killer as she ran wild over the long rollers like a headstrong horse with the bit in its teeth.

When the time came for him to think about how to earn a living, he chose something connected with the sea and the ships. He might be apprenticed to a sailmaker or a shipwright, or he could learn how to make ropes or cables or casks. If he had an eye for beautiful things, and a quick hand, he could learn how to carve the lovely figureheads which glided over the water on the bows of every square-rigger. A knowing eye for the color of hot iron would surely send him to the forges to learn about chain-making, or bolts, or anchors, while a good head for figures would see him perched on a tall stool in one of the counting houses, keeping track of the manifests and cargoes, the profits and losses of the voyages.

Most of all however, he would have his eye on the ships themselves. If he were strong and healthy and deep-chested, by the time he was finished with school at thirteen or fourteen, he would be pestering his father to find him a berth as an apprentice seaman. He well knew that if he had a sharp Yankee eye for the trading and the profits, and the knack of command, he could rise to be a captain before he was twenty.

He learned also to reckon with the great shipowners— Mr. Derby, Mr. Grey, Mr. Crowninshield, and others. These were names he learned as he learned to speak. He knew that somehow he must impress these men with his skill so that when the time came, and he was ready, they would know he could be trusted with one of their ships. Like old-time lords of the castle, these men ruled the little town of Salem. As their fortunes went, so went the fortunes of everyone else.

The ships, the owners, and the seamen had made Salem the most important port in America. The vessels traveled to the far corners of the earth, carrying nails, shoes, cloth, pots, pans, clocks, tools, furniture and all the other things which American work and ingenuity produced. They returned after a year, two years, sometimes three years or even more, after they had sailed. If they'd been lucky they came home fat with profits, deeply laden and heavy with coffee, spices, silks, and all manner of fabulous and valuable goods from across the oceans. Salem enterprise and sea sense were helping America get on her feet. The ships carried the word of Yankee skill and ability to the whole world. So far and so wide did the ships travel that the inhabitants of many a distant port or island called the whole outside world "Salem"—the word carved across the counters of the ships, the only word they had ever heard for lands other than their own.

Yes, in those days, all good things came to a young man from the sea—his career, his fortune—if he were lucky—and even a pretty wife to boot. Every Salem lass cocked her bonnet and cast a quick, merry eye to the wind for a broad-shouldered young mate or captain to wed.

The boy who stood gazing out over Salem harbor knew and felt all these things. He was a Salem boy, born and reared on the bay. The sea, the sky, the ships, the sun, and the stars were all a part of him, and the safe return of a big square-rigger home was an event which stirred him deeply. He shivered a bit. In spite of the warm sun, the breeze was cool and his clothes were thin and old.

He ran on until finally, puffing and panting, he was tearing full speed down Derby Street, around the corner of a warehouse, to the wharf itself. A big crowd was on hand.

The ship was very close now. She glided up the channel slower and slower, scarcely disturbing the glassy water or raising a single ripple. She seemed like a ghost ship, moving without effort, without sound of any kind.

A tiny monkey, a curio brought from some strange land, swung excitedly through the rigging. His chattering "chee, chee" came clearly to the people across the narrowing gap of water. And, just as out of place as the monkey in this businesslike New England seaport, a huge green and orange parrot perched on the taffrail. The bird stared in alarm at the strange goings-on on the dock, and let out piercing squawks, to the delight of all the youngsters.

Suddenly the yards on the masts were braced around and the sails were clear aback, pressing against the masts. The ship slowed to nearly a dead stop, but drifted always nearer.

Aft on the poop deck the captain was a splendid sight in his most elegant cutaway frock coat and stovepipe plug hat. He carefully estimated the speed and position of his vessel and at precisely the right moment he murmured an order to the first mate standing beside him. It was beneath the dignity of a captain to bellow an order but this was one of the attributes of a good second-in-command. The first mate gave out with a roar that shook the rigging and in a second the men were swarming over the decks and clambering aloft like cats.

Another order and the yards came down smartly with a furious squealing of blocks and pulleys. White canvas fluttered and quickly the ship was without a rag on her, all sails neatly furled. While this was going on, other seamen in the bow and stern sent heaving lines streaking like snakes through the air to the docks.

The light heaving lines were grabbed by excited men and boys who quickly pulled the heavy mooring ropes attached to them ashore. The eyes of the heavy ropes were dropped over the bollards along the edge of the pier.

Now a final order, a joyful hurricane bellow from the first mate: "Man the capstan!" The seamen on the bow started to tramp around the capstan and those in the waist of the ship commenced to heave powerfully and in rhythm on the mooring ropes. Slowly the ship warped up to the dock.

Soon a voice of one of the sailors took up a chant. It was joined by the voices of the rest of the crew. The chant was an old one, a chant of homecoming and of happiness at the prospect of release from long and often bitter labor. A grand thing it was to hear the rough voices of the men of a deep-water sailing ship growling and echoing over the people and the town, like the beat of the ocean itself.

> "I thought I heard the Captain say,
> Leave her Johnnie, leave her.
> Tomorrow you will get your pay,
> It's time for you to leave her.
> The work was hard, the voyage long,
> Leave her Johnnie, leave her.
> The food was bad, the wages low,
> It's time for us to leave her.
> The seas were high, the gales were strong,
> Leave her Johnnie, leave her.
> And now ashore again we'll go,
> It's time for us to leave her.
> The sails are furled, the work is done,
> Leave her Johnnie, leave her.
> Now ashore we'll have some fun,
> It's time for us to leave her."

With a flourish and a stomp on the last line, the sailors warped the ship to the dock and snugged down the lines. The *Java* was home in Salem at last, after two years of wandering over far, deep waters.

There was a moment of silence, as though the sea-weary vessel and her crew could scarcely realize they were home, and as though the people on the dock could not really understand that all their hopes and good dreams had returned safely at last. The silence passed and then a great roar of welcome rose as people searched for familiar, loved faces and exchanged jokes and greetings.

A gangplank was run out to the ship and secured. The door to the big warehouse opened and the crowd respectfully cleared a passage. Old Elias Hasket Derby, owner of the *Java,* walked slowly across the dock. Though he tried to be stern and forbidding, as befitted his position, his eyes were alight. In his scrawny old neck, red and wrinkled like the neck of a turkey buzzard, his Adam's apple jumped and bounced. Even austere Elias Derby could not wholly control his emotion at the sight of one of his largest ships safely home and deep with cargo. In honor of the event, he had dressed in his finest apparel—bright purple-plum colored waistcoat, dark green jacket with silver buttons, and fine, tight-fitting brown trousers. He carried a big, silver-headed cane and as he crossed the gangplank he limped heavily from the gout.

Elias Derby was welcomed at the head of the gangplank by the captain. They shook hands formally, then solemnly walked aft and vanished into the cabin below. Here they would discuss the voyage and the cargo and most likely drink a good many glasses of fine Madeira wine brought home especially for this joyful occasion.

☆

Two

The boy worked his way through the crowd to the edge of the dock. He stared up at the towering stern of the *Java*. The first mate was standing by the rail talking to the grizzled old bos'n.

"Ahoy," bellowed the boy, in his best imitation of a salt-water shellback. "Ahoy Henry Prince. Henry . . . down here."

Prince turned, grinned down at him. "Ahoy yourself, Nat Bowditch. Come aboard," he shouted. "I've brought you something."

Henry Prince was a young man, tall, spar-shouldered, powerful. He was perhaps eighteen years of age, and when he walked he moved heavily but at the same time with great certainty and grace. His mouth was wide and laughing; his eyes were blue and serious and quiet with the weight of responsibility—except when he smiled. Then they had a daring, devil-may-care look to them.

Nat squeezed up the dock to the gangplank and crossed over to the *Java*. He dropped lightly to the holystoned deck. Already the scene was one of great activity. The crew had knocked out the wedges and were removing the strongbacks over the hatches to take off the tarpaulins and covers. Later, men from ashore would start the unloading.

Up from the holds came the good smells of the cargo, mixing strongly with the salty bite of Salem harbor air. Out of the hatches rose the scents of coffee, pepper, cinnamon, cloves, aromatic woods, the musk of silks and satins and a hundred other fragrances. It seemed like a breath from across the ocean itself, straight from lands where surf hissed and thundered on snow-white beaches, and palm trees nodded to the trade winds.

Nat hesitated a moment by the open main hatch, deeply breathing the odors. Then, suddenly, his mind darted into another channel. Soon his head was filled with numbers, translating everything about the cargo into columns of figures, into addition, subtraction, multiplication, and division. The numbers flew through his head in a swirling tide of calculations in which he computed weights, values, units of money, money exchange of foreign countries, duties, and many other things. A bellow shocked him from his dreaming.

"Nat," roared Prince. "What are you waiting for, boy?"

And then, because he was on board at the invitation of the first mate himself and was quite the envy of all the other boys on the dock, Nathaniel Bowditch wasted no more time. Quickly and in a businesslike manner, he headed aft.

In a moment he was shaking hands with Henry Prince. Nat had known Henry all his life. The older boy had taken a liking to spindly little Nat Bowditch, and in spite of the difference in their ages, the two had tramped the fields and beaches of Salem for nearly as long as either could remember. Henry had gone to sea when he was fourteen, and so in the last few years they had only seen each other at rare intervals.

"What's the news, Nat?" asked Henry.

Nat paid no attention. "Tell me about the voyage, Henry. Any real bad gales? Did you lose any men? How did the ship behave?" Questions tumbled from his lips.

"Not so fast, not so fast, Sir. First you must tell me all about Salem." Henry was avid for news of home. "Later we'll talk about the voyage. How's your mother?"

Nat fell silent. "She died last winter, Henry," he managed to say. "It was very cold . . . during a winter blizzard." He could not go on. How could he say that his mother had died of tuberculosis, and from cold, and from the lack of food and care, in spite of everything that he could do?

"I'm sorry, Nat. So sorry," said Henry quietly. And then, "How's your father? Your brothers and sisters?"

"Father's ashore now. He can't go to sea. He has a cooper's shop and I live with him. The others . . . the others are just staying with people we know."

In those times, when families were broken, children were simply taken without question by neighbors and relatives. There was no complaint and no time wasted in too much pity. Life was hard; it had to move on in spite of grief and loss. Youngsters simply went where they were

[24]

told and somehow grew up to make the best they could of their lives.

Prince was thoughtful a moment in sympathy and then again he said, "I'm terribly sorry, Nat, but you must do the best you can and always try to behave as your mother would have liked. Now cheer up. Come below and see what I've brought you." He led the way down the ladder to his cabin.

They went through the main saloon for the officers of the ship. Nat paused a moment to look about him, thrilled by the orderly, shipshape beauty. The bulkheads were paneled in glowing mahogany and rosewood. On the sideboard, the mirror, the glassware, the silver, and the brasswork were polished and gleamed elegantly in comparison to the dark woods. Directly over the captain's chair at the head of the table, a compass was swung from the overhead. Not even during mealtime would the master be relieved of his responsibility. He must know at all times the course and position of his ship. Along one bulkhead was the gun rack, displaying a long row of polished and oiled muskets and cutlasses. A merchant ship in far-off waters, and sometimes even in waters more "civilized" frequently had to defend herself to the best of her ability.

Nat walked past the weapons rack and followed Prince down a passageway, into his cabin.

Henry rummaged in a locker and took out a long musical instrument. It looked like a flute except that it had a flare at one end. It reminded Nat of a thin speaking trumpet.

"It's a flute," said Henry. "From India. The kind they

use to hypnotize poisonous snakes and make them do tricks."

Nat was incredulous. "You're teasing. Make poisonous snakes do *tricks?*"

"Indeed they do. They make them sway and do sort of a dance. Makes your blood run cold when you know that one bite from the fangs of such serpents could do you in."

Nat put the flute to his mouth and blew. A soft, mournful little sound came from it.

"You'll have to practice up a bit," said Henry. "Then maybe you can find some snakes to charm. Or some young ladies when you're a bit older."

Just then they were interrupted by a voice calling from the main saloon. "Mr. Prince. Mr. Henry Prince. Come here, please."

Even though the voice said "please," there was nothing polite about it. There was no mistaking the anger in Elias Derby's summons, nor its ring of authority.

Henry hurried into the saloon, and Nat was right behind him.

Mr. Derby and Captain Gibaut stood by the table, and Mr. Derby was so furious and so red in the face that it seemed he must die of apoplexy on the spot. Poor Captain Gibaut, a very dignified captain, with long, bushy sideburns, was most ill at ease.

"Mr. Prince," said the shipowner, his Adam's apple hopping up and down like a frightened monkey, "apparently I am sending my ships to sea in command of lubbers and fools. Not a soul in this vessel to be trusted."

He looked at them severely. Nat shivered in his boots.

Derby continued, sputtering. His thin lower lip jutted out and curled up until his whole mouth was bound into

a tight little ball. "Unbelievable . . . absolutely unbelievable. The *Java* entrusted to this man who calls himself
a shipmaster . . . and lost to pirates off Tripoli."

"But . . . but, sir, we were able to recapture her,"
stammered the unlucky Captain Gibaut.

"Largely through your first mate's efforts, I'll wager,"
said Derby. He turned to Prince. "Is this correct, sir?"

Prince was extremely uncomfortable. "Well, sir. Not
precisely. You see, sir . . ."

Derby interrupted again, stamping down with his cane
on the deck. "I'm not interested in explanations, young
man." He returned to Captain Gibaut. "And you, sir.
This is not the point, that the *Java* was retaken. A properly organized vessel would not have been lost to begin
with. You may consider yourself fortunate, sir, that I do
not relieve you of your command."

He took a small, golden snuffbox from his pocket, helped
himself to a generous pinch. Nat watched in fascination
as the sneeze worked itself up and finally exploded in a
shattering clap of thunder. Derby rocked under the impact,
finally steadied himself at the table. Now his old blue eyes,
streaming with tears, fastened their furious glance on the
boy.

"And who are you, sir? What are you doing aboard my
ship?"

"This is—" Prince started to say, but Derby cut him
short.

"Let him answer for himself, Mr. Prince. If he can
speak. Now, you, boy. Who are you?"

Nat wanted to drop right through the deck. He managed to blurt out, "Nat . . . that is, Nathaniel. Nathaniel
Bowditch, sir."

"Bowditch. Bowditch." The old man searched his memory. "Ah yes. Bowditch. I knew your grandfather well. Fine a shipmaster as ever sailed from this port. Can't say as much for your father. Habbakuk's the name isn't it?"

Nat nodded miserably.

"Now, your mother. She would be Catherine Bowditch. Distant relative of my wife, I believe. Died last winter, I understand. My sympathy, sir." No event in the town was so small it did not come to the attention of Elias Derby. He looked at the diminutive, forlorn little boy. His countenance softened, but just slightly. "You need some beef on your bones, boy." With this he dismissed Nat and turned to the companionway. Halfway up, he looked back and addressed Prince.

"When you are clear of your duties here, please pay me a visit in my office. In spite of the mismanagement aboard this vessel, it may be you are ready for command, sir." Derby stumped his way to the deck above and was gone.

Captain Gibaut looked at his first mate. He shook his head in bafflement, mopped his brow with a huge silk handkerchief. "Whew. Whew. My dear goodness, sir," he said. Then he remembered his manners and went up the ladder to escort Mr. Derby ashore.

Nat could hardly hold back the questions. "Were you really captured by pirates and had to fight to get the ship back? And will he really discharge poor Captain Gibaut?"

Prince laughed. "We had a brush with a felucca off Tripoli, but as you can plainly see, we got the *Java* back. So what's the difference? Nothing lost but some powder and ball and that's what they're for. Don't worry about Captain Gibaut. He's one of the best masters in Salem and the old buzzard knows it. Wait'll he sees the cargo. Run to five hundred per cent profit if a penny."

"Then why is Mr. Derby so angry?"

"Ho, ho, Nat," said Henry. "You've got a lot to learn. A man doesn't get to be the owner of a fleet of ships like Derby's by being pleasant. No siree. Got to find things to shout about just to keep people on their toes. You see, Derby's never had a voyage out of the *Java* like this one. We're in perfect shape. Not a man or spar lost in two years and I told you how valuable the cargo is. But Derby's *got* to find something to complain about. It's the nature of shipowners. And the only thing he could find was that little run-in with the pirates."

Nat pondered a moment on the strange ways of old men in general, and old shipowners in particular. "What does he want you for?" he wondered.

"Probably wants me to tell him the story of the pirates all over again. Derby loves to hear tall tales of his ships."

"And do you really . . . really think he means to give you a command of your own?"

Henry Prince lost his gay mood. This was a very serious matter. "It may be. It just may be," he said slowly.

"And, Henry," cried Nat, now in excitement, "if he does give you a ship . . . take me . . . take me with you. Let me sail with you, Henry. Please." The whole world would be different, and seemed so already, just at the thought of getting to sea.

Prince looked down at the lonely little boy. He saw the hope shining in the deep-set eyes. He was tempted, but then he also saw the short, frail, thin body, the narrow shoulders. There could be no compromise; the truth had to be faced. "No, Nat," he said. "You're not old enough."

"But Henry, I'll soon be fourteen. I don't want any more schooling. My brother William was my age when he sailed. So were you." Nat's desire was almost unbearable.

Again Prince looked at his young friend and again he was tempted to give in. Once again though, he took the hard, truthful course.

"Nat," he said, "don't think of it. You're too small. You don't know what it's like at sea. The ships are for the big, husky lads. The life is hard. Stay home and learn to do something else with your life than to sail a full-rigged ship."

Nat pulled himself up to full height. It wasn't very much, but what he lacked in size he made up in temper.

"I am big enough. I'm stronger than you think. I want to go to sea and I will go to sea. I'll not be stuck in Salem. You and your big stupid muscles. You're all the same. Every one of you. You sail the most beautiful ships in the world but you're a bunch of dull oxen. Muscles! That's all that counts with you."

Nat had lost control of himself and was fairly screaming in fury. He threw himself at Prince, who promptly grabbed him and held him tightly. This was an old story. Many, many times Henry Prince had held the boy until he had cooled down.

"Now simmer off, Nat," he said, "and I'll let you go."

Finally Nat stopped in exhaustion, and Prince promptly released him. "Have dinner with me tonight, Nat," he said. "I'll tell you all about the pirates."

Nat looked at his old friend suspiciously. The bait of dinner aboard the *Java* was tempting, but he refused to take it. There was the matter of his dignity. "No," he

[30]

said. "Stories are for children. I'll come back aboard a ship of yours only when I'm a member of her crew."

Very formally Nat stalked to the ladder. Then he paused, a flicker of a grin passing over his face. He never stayed angry for very long. "And besides," he said, "there is talk in the town that First Officer Henry Prince may have some courting to do first night ashore." With that he left.

Prince grinned, watched the little figure in the ill-fitting clothes scrambling up the ladder. Then he grimaced in exasperation. There was nothing he could do. He loved this stubborn, hot-tempered little boy dearly, but he knew there was no place aboard a full-rigged ship for him. At least not now.

Three

Spring, with its green hills and blue seas and skies, had gone. The days in Salem stretched through the long warm summer and fall into the winter. With winter came cold, and terrible gray storms and blizzards that lashed and blinded the coast.

One day late in January, Nat Bowditch stood alone on Derby wharf and gazed sadly out to sea. Under short-ened canvas a square-rigged ship stood into the Atlantic. The dark rectangles of its sails swung in enormous arcs, nearly from horizon to horizon it seemed, as the vessel lunged and wallowed through the heaving rollers. The speck of its hull was half-obscured in the driving spray. Henry Prince had his command and was outward bound.

Quick to flare with temper, Nat was equally quick to forget. He and Henry Prince had long since made up their quarrel but in spite of all that Nat could do or say, his friend steadfastly refused to give in out of sympathy and take him on the voyage. Although it was a terrible pill to swallow, in his heart Nat knew that Prince was probably right. There was no place for him before the mast on a sailing vessel.

Nevertheless, the disappointment was almost unbearable. As Nat watched the lonely dot of the ship finally vanish into the murk and gloom of the winter squalls, he felt that a dream had died, and with it a part of himself also. His dream of going to sea at last truly did seem dead. If an old and good friend like Captain Henry Prince could not make room for him on his own ship, then what could Nat expect from anyone else?

In spite of all the resolve that Nat could muster, tears stung his eyes. He didn't especially love the sea, as did some boys his age. He knew also that he really was too small and light for the backbreaking work on braces and halyards and in the rigging. But without quite being able to put his finger on the reason, he knew that he was deeply moved by the stately beauty of the great vessels and their soaring clouds of sail. There must be something that a man who didn't have the build of an ox could do aboard them. Nat's jaw set. His thin shoulders squared with determination. *I am going . . . I shall . . . I shall . . .* he promised himself. Then he turned from the deserted dock and walked quickly back up into the town, to the cooperage of his father, Habbakuk Bowditch.

Habbakuk had been trained in his youth as a cooper, but, like all the Bowditch men before him, he had eventually wound up going to sea. He had risen to be a respected shipmaster, but now, perhaps as a result of the fact that he had lost two vessels, he could no longer get a command. He had gone back to his original occupation of making casks and barrels.

Habbakuk was known in the town as a good, kindly man but unlucky and ineffectual. He was also known for his knowledge of the scriptures and was famous for his amazing consumption of rum, taken, so he said, to "make him forget the awful sights he had seen at sea."

When his wife died, as was rumored, from cold and lack of proper food, and the rest of the family was parceled out to relatives and friends, Habbakuk had kept little Nathaniel. They lived at the cooperage, and he was trying to train his son at this trade.

Nat returned from saying good-by to Henry Prince and immediately got back to his work. He was making a barrel. Round and round he went, carefully doing just exactly as his father had taught him, fitting the staves into the hoops. Suddenly the whole thing fell apart into a tangle of oaken kindling at his feet.

Habbakuk, who was watching, shook his head in despair. "No, no, Nat," he said. "Why can you not seem to grasp the knack of it?"

He stood looking in sorrow at this diminutive but well-loved youngest son, who couldn't seem to learn even as simple a thing as making a barrel. His other sons were big and strong and intelligent and already properly apprenticed before the mast. With luck and industry they could look forward to good careers. But this one! This one was a trial. Catherine, bless her, before she died, used to say that little Nat was going to amount to "something definite." Habbakuk sighed. Whatever it was, he did wish

[34]

fervently that "something definite" would show signs of making its appearance.

He picked up the staves from the floor and arranged them quickly and solidly within the circle of hoops. "There," he said. "Don't you see how easy it is? All you have to do is do it right." He rubbed his forehead in exasperation, reached to a shelf, took down a small brown rum jug. Tipping the jug back, he helped himself to a small restorative drop and replaced it on the shelf.

Habbakuk wiped his mouth and chin on the back of his hand and looked at his son. His exasperation was gone, and he said kindly, "But it's no use telling you again and again if you haven't got the gumption to learn."

Nat mumbled something. Shame was written all over his face.

Thinking aloud, Habbakuk continued. "What am I to do with you, boy? You've no talent for farm work. You're too puny for the ships and heaven knows you're all thumbs for a trade. What would you like to do, Nathaniel?"

Nat hung his head in unhappiness. Then his father straightened up, brushed the sawdust and shavings from his clothes. "Something's got to be done, boy. How are you to earn your living?"

"I don't know, Father," Nat said miserably.

Habbakuk took another sampling of the rum jug. "I've been thinking," he said. "There's one thing yet we haven't tried. You can read and write and you seem to have a tolerable good head for your sums. Perhaps through them there's a way for you to earn your daily bread."

Without saying another word, Habbakuk left the cooperage. Little Nat sat wrapped in black gloom. As far as he could tell, if he couldn't learn how to do something soon to make a living he imagined he'd probably starve to death. The future seemed black indeed. He couldn't farm. He couldn't go to sea. And now he couldn't even learn to make barrels. Even this stupid cask had defeated him. He eyed it darkly and in sudden disgust aimed a swift kick at the mass of staves. They answered back with a soggy boom.

In spite of his despair and his hatred for the cask, all of an instant he became fascinated by it. Its perfect geometric proportions literally leaped right out at him. Without even being conscious of it, he began turning the barrel into numbers!

He estimated the diameter of the half-finished barrel. He counted the staves, tried to imagine each as the end of the spokes of a wheel whose hub was at the center. Oblivious of everything else now, Nat dropped to his knees and began tracing out with his fingers numbers in the sawdust on the floor, trying to calculate the angle between each spoke of this imaginery wheel. There his father found him when he returned several hours later.

In his travels about the village, Habbakuk had by now visited a goodly number of taverns and had taken on a considerable cargo of good West Indies rum. Between stops at the taverns, however, he had been very busy making the necessary arrangements to enable Nat to earn his living. He now explained.

He had apprenticed the boy to a firm of ship chandlers in town, Ropes & Hodges. Nat was a little dubious as to what this might mean exactly, but he cheered up when he learned that among his other duties he would be expected to keep the books for the store. Anything that

[36]

had to do with numbers would be easy and might even be fun in the bargain.

Nat didn't know anything about bookkeeping, but Habbakuk had taken care of this too. He had enrolled his son in a special school in Salem run by one Michael Walsh. Here young boys who were to be apprenticed as clerks and accountants were given training. Considering Nat's head for figures, Habbakuk had allowed that a couple of months in Walsh's school would teach him all that he needed to know to take care of the ledgers of his future employers.

Nat wasn't to be paid anything for his work at the chandlery, but this was the usual arrangement. Apprentices were grateful for the opportunity to learn a trade. He was, however, to be supplied with food, lodging, and clothes.

Soon Nat had finished his course in bookkeeping at Walsh's and was installed in his new job. He was twelve years old at the time and was bound for nine years. He would be a free man again at the age of twenty-one.

He was very pleased with his lot. He slept in a small room in the attic in the home of one of the partners— Jonathan Hodges. From this high vantage point, when he was not working Nat could see everything that was going on in the harbor—the arrivals and departures of ships, the constant bustle of loading and unloading, and hear the shouts and cries of carousing sailormen as they celebrated their release from long months at sea. From here also he had a grand view of the majestic storms and the great white blizzards that in the winter poured smoking in over the town out of the north and east. And in fine weather, from the little garret room Nat could stare into the deep heavens above him and soar in his imagination through the clear starlit and moonlit sky.

There were other advantages too in his new life. The people to whom he was bound were decent, kindly folks. Possibly for the first time in his life he was warmly, if not elegantly, clothed. And also possibly for the first time, he was able to eat his fill regularly.

When Mr. and Mrs. Hodges wanted to go out for an evening, Nat often filled in as baby-sitter. As he sat in the big, comfortable kitchen, reading by the light of an oil lamp, listening to the comfortable crackle of the fire in the kitchen range, and occasionally giving the crib a rock when the baby was restless or fretful, the world indeed seemed very easy and good.

Nat had lots of work to do. The hours in the chandlery were long and often ran over into the evenings. Occasionally, however, he had the chance to kick up his heels. With other young fellows about town he indulged to the fullest in the rather mild entertainment and pastimes available. There was choir singing in the church. Weekly dances. Nighttime picnics when the weather was good. The intriguing spectacle when all the bums and drunkards were rounded up, put in a cart, and taken out to the edge of town, hopefully never to return. He also learned to play his flute and in the company of young friends, spent long evenings making music and having the fun that was normal to his age and times.

Nat's real life though, centered more and more about the chandlery. He tended the books of course, and he swept the place out, kept the shelves in order and helped wait on the customers. He enjoyed every bit of it but the finest thing was that now, instead of being just an observer of the activities of the port, he was a part of them, even if a small and quite unimportant part. He was closer and closer to the world of the sea and the ships. Everything he sold, or saw, or did was alive with the breath and the surge of the ocean.

The customers were nearly all mates and captains. Some were dressed in elegant shore-going clothes—cutaway jackets, top hats, silk shirts with ruffled or lace fronts, richly colored vests and trousers. Others wore the working clothes of their calling—dark trousers, dark pea-jackets with perhaps brass buttons, dark caps, and possibly brightly colored checked shirts. Some sported a golden earring in one ear; some carried fancy canes with great silver knobs; still others had a tiny green or blue parrot, or a bright-eyed little monkey perched on a broad shoulder and tethered by a thin silver chain. Almost all were big, powerful men, narrow-hipped, with great, bulging shoulders, bronzed faces, deep chests, and the look of faraway horizons in their eyes. To such men as these from the ships Nat sold compasses, salt pork and log books, sail twine, huge coffeepots, canvas, nuts, bolts, needles and palms, copper nails, and marling spikes; and to the navigators, the ones Nat liked best because they dealt in figures, he sold sextants and dividers and protractors and Gunter's scales—the forerunner of slide rules—which were used in their mysterious calculations.

Best of all, Nat liked to make deliveries or run errands. He clambered importantly aboard the ships themselves and wandered freely through the wood and sawdust fragrant yards where other ships were being built. He loved the sail lofts where sailmakers laid out the canvas to chalk marks on the vast, shining floors and then patiently fashioned the confused tangles in giant, precise, lovely squares and triangles that someday would billow in the wind and drive Salem ships all over the world. And other days he stared fascinated in long, narrow rooms, like hallways almost, where quiet, silent men plied still another trade, walking slowly up and down, back and forth, twisting golden hemp fibers into strong rope.

And so the time passed. The months rolled by into a year. Nat observed the life of the port, he played his flute, he had what fun he could. He also worked very hard at his job and made himself valuable, especially with his ability to manage numbers. There was nothing he could not do when it came to figures. And it was a truly wonderful discovery too, when it slowly began to dawn on him that the numbers he loved so much were only symbols for objects and that, marvelously, the relationship between things and objects could be so beautifully and easily expressed in the figures that represented them.

And then, all of a sudden, without any reason, Nat began to study! Other more fortunate boys of the town were preparing to enter that struggling little school of "higher education" up in Boston—Harvard. No such luck for Nat Bowditch. Perhaps he envied these luckier boys; perhaps he didn't have time to think about them. In any event, it made no difference. Harvard was not for him. Anything he was going to learn from books would have to be done on his own—in spare time at the chandlery, at night in his garret room, or downstairs in the kitchen minding the Hodges' baby.

He developed a system for studying, and this system was the only one that seemed logical to his orderly, mathematical mind. A person simply started at the beginning

of something and went calmly straight through to the end!
Sometimes this took him into comical pathways. For
example, he had access to a set of encyclopedias. The set
bore the impressive name of *Chambers Cyclopedia, Or
an Universal Dictionary of the Arts and Sciences by
E. Chambers, F.R.S. With Supplement and Improvements by Abraham Rees, F.R.S.*

The fearsome title didn't bother Nat in the least. He
simply settled down to study the four huge volumes. He
did it not by dividing the information up into subjects
that interested him, or were related to each other. He did
it by starting right at the beginning and plowing straight
through to the end. He didn't know any other way to
study. One simply took books and read them! Nat absorbed
what he could from *Chambers* and the mass of information it offered, jumbled and mixed up as it was, all the way
from A to Z. And that was that.

So the first year rolled by. He developed, he progressed,
he worked. He learned to love knowledge, especially
mathematics. But this was all. There was no rhyme or
reason, no direction to what he studied. There was no end,
no goal. This all changed suddenly, and in a very strange
way.

Shortly after his thirteenth year, when he had "finished"
with *Chambers Cyclopedia,* he was sent out on an errand
to deliver beeswax to the sail loft. The sailmakers used
the wax to draw across the twine to make it supple and
strong and waterproof and to glide more easily through
the heavy canvas. The afternoon was beautiful and blus-
tery, and on an impulse Nat decided to make a detour past
Derby wharf.

A wharf where oceangoing ships tie up is like no other place on earth. It is a kind of never-never place, a no-man's land, a link between the ocean and the shore but belonging to neither. Even a ship tied up to a wharf, bringing with it as it does the savor of the deep ocean, cannot alter this feeling of a wharf, or claim it as its own, or make it a part of the sea. The reason for this is that a ship at a pier is but a temporary object, a poor tethered thing, enduring its lot in silence and only waiting to be rid of its indignity and to return to its natural habitat. It does not affect the lonely identity of the wharf.

This afternoon, though, Derby wharf had a different feel to it. It was lonely, empty. No ship was in port. The great doors of the warehouse were shut. No one was about except one dark-clad figure of a man sitting on one of the big mooring bollards. Behind the man there was nothing but blue—blue, white-capped sea and blue sky specked by a few circling birds. It was quiet too, with no sound but the gentle wash of the tide and the occasional cry of a gull.

Nat stopped short a moment, puzzled. Why did the wharf seem different today? Instead of being only the connection between land and sea, today it was simply and without any fuss, a part of the sea. He peered about him, trying to solve this riddle. Suddenly he knew the answer.

The sense of the wide-open sea that overpowered Derby wharf came from the solitary figure sitting on the bollard. Nat softly approached. The figure turned.

It was an old man. There was no doubt now that it was he who brought the far pastures of blue water to the wharf. They were in the cut of his trousers, in his short jacket that looked as though it was made of velvet, in his blue-checked shirt, in the broad-brimmed, varnished hat that perched securely on his heavily tarred hair, and in the huge, gnarled hands that rested quietly in his lap. Most of all the sea was in his leathery face, with the spiderweb of pink wrinkles about the eyes, and in the eyes themselves, small and blue and clear and washed clean and faded by a thousand winds and suns and rains.

Who was it? The Old Man of the Sea? Father Neptune himself? Or the Flying Dutchman? Nat felt a prickle of fear ripple down his back, but then it vanished as the man spoke. This was no apparition but just an old sailor-man tossed up on the wharf. Furthermore, he spoke with a broad British accent.

"Good afternoon, lad," the sailor said politely.

Nat bobbed his head.

"And what might your name be?"

"Nathaniel Bowditch."

"The same Bowditches as has that ugly reef of black rocks named for 'em at the entrance to the harbor?"

Nat shifted uncomfortably. Nobody could be very proud of the fact that one of his ancestors had lost his ship there and that from then on the dread menace to navigation was named after his family.

"Yes, sir," he said. "My grandfather drove a ship ashore there. Bowditch's Reef. That's it."

"Nothing to be ashamed of, lad. Happens to the best." The old man's eyes twinkled as he gazed at Nat. "But I can see you're not a sailorman. Too puny. What do you do?"

"I'm an apprentice. Only a bookkeeper in the chandlery."

"Don't apologize. Every man to what he does best. But wouldn't you like to sail in the big ones?"

Nat shrugged helplessly.

The sailor examined the thin little figure standing before him. "There's more than one way to splice a rope," he said kindly. "So you're a bookkeeper. Must have a good head for figures. Never forget your sums, do you?"

Nat's eyes brightened. "No, sir."

"Then why don't you learn to be a navigator?"

The idea was a new one to Nat. "Navigation?"

"Sure. Why not?"

"But *sailors* navigate ships," Nat said in wonderment. "Not bookkeepers."

"Oh yes, they do all right. And they're pretty bad at their job. Wander all over the earth like ants. Back and forth. Here and there. Never know where they are. That's right, just like ants in the grass. Crazy."

"But I don't see what that's got to do with bookkeeping."

"Lad, ships should be *sailed* by sailors but navigated by numbers. That's all there is to navigation. Numbers. Distances, angles, degrees around the earth." The old sailor jerked a thumb up to the sky. "The stars. The moon, the sun. All their paths through the heavens. Just numbers. Get 'em right and you can take any ship anywhere. Two and two's four. Ashore and at sea. The time's coming when that's how they'll do it."

Nat had heard about this and he had also heard how many a good mariner had lost his ship and been disgraced because he'd tried to navigate by numbers instead of trusting to his own good sea sense.

"But people laugh at . . . at . . . arithmetic at sea."

"Of course they do. And they do drive their ships ashore trusting in it. But that's because sailors don't know enough about it yet. But they will. New ways will be invented and they'll learn. Arithmetic sailors will do it for them."

"Arithmetic sailors." Nat repeated the words. Somehow they didn't sound very good.

"And why not? Lad, I don't know much about it, but you get a slate and a pencil and a copybook. I'll show you some things."

From now on Nat's life changed. The old man was far from being the simple ignorant sailor he seemed. He had been an officer on a British frigate who had jumped ship in Boston during the American Revolution. He knew just about everything that had to do with the mathematics of navigation of the times, and he explained it to Nat.

The boy's mind was like a dry sponge. He soaked it all up, and in the process he blossomed. Numbers, figures, arithmetic. Now they had a use, a real use connected with ships, if one could only learn how to manipulate them. The old man taught Nat just about all that was known of numbers navigation of the times. Logarithms. Trigonometry. It was all easy for the boy, and he discovered a thrill he had never felt before when he learned how to relate his beloved numbers to the vast heavens above. The eternal swing of the sun and the moon and the stars never varied and from their positions in the skies, from the distances between them, from the angles they made with the earth and with each other, positions on the globe could be determined.

The weeks went by and Nat continued to absorb it all. In his room, in the kitchen at home, in the chandlery itself, day and night, he pored over his slate, puzzling out the relationships between numbers and the heavenly bodies. They were steady and sure, and as he began to see the majesty of astronomy, his mind rejoiced over the unerring logic and order of mathematics.

He began to put it all together, and to do things on his own. He made an almanac. He made a sundial. He built wooden and wire triangles, spheres, models of the heavens. And then another wonderful thing happened.

His older brother William was going to sea and preparing himself for an officer's berth. He didn't have Nat's razor-sharp mind for figures but he was interested to learn what he could of the science of navigation. He had enrolled in a local school of "navigation," such as it was, and one afternoon he stopped by the chandlery.

"Nat," he said, "they've got a new book at the school."

Nat looked up.

"Yep," said William. "It's about a thing called *algebra*. Its a way to solve mathematical problems with letters instead of numbers."

Nat didn't hesitate about this. "Get it for me, William," he pleaded.

Later William came back with the book. "Look, Nat," he said. "You can only have it for tonight. I have to take it back in the morning."

Next day Nat wasn't much good at his job in the store. He was half asleep most of the day. The reason was that he had stayed up all night, completely enthralled by the beauty and unassailable logic of algebra!

As time passed, the white-hot quest for knowledge took precedence over everything else in Nat's life. Almost in bewilderment he followed its light. Helplessly he obeyed its summons and drifted deeper and deeper into his books. When he was fourteen, he wrote in his journal "I am seeing too many people. Wasting too much time." He didn't, of course, cut out all friendships, but by the time he was sixteen or seventeen, there was no doubt that boyhood and youth were gone, with their carefree fun. He had little time for anything but studies.

But *now* he ran into a stone wall. There was nothing more in Salem for him to study. He had gone far beyond the town's resources in mathematics—particularly the mathematics of astronomy. Nat was ready for something new, and it came. It came because of an event that had taken place years before, during the Revolutionary War.

Four

Beverly was a small seaport directly across the bay from Salem. Its sailors prided themselves on being as daring as any along the Massachusetts coast. They were especially proud of the reputation they had made during the war as privateers, when many a fat British merchantman fell victim to their seamanship and accurate gunnery.

One moonlit night in 1780, the captain of a Beverly privateer took his fast little ship right under the noses of patroling British warships in the Irish Sea. When he sighted a large ship some miles distant across the glistening water, he didn't hesitate. He cracked on sail and ran out his guns.

When the engagement was over, his prize crew discovered a cargo of little value. Included in it, however, was one item which was a real oddity. It was the entire library of the famous Irish scientist, Richard Kirwan. The many books dealt with the entire range of man's knowledge in chemistry, physics, astronomy, philosophy, and mathematics.

As was usual, back in Beverly, the captured cargo was put up for auction. An apothecary bought the library. Paper was short in America during the war and he had the novel idea that the pages in the big folios would do very nicely for wrapping parcels.

In those times, the best-educated men in any town were the preachers. So it was in Salem. A group organized the Philosophical Library Company, bought all of Kirwan's books, and housed them in the home of Reverend John Prince. In this manner, the rough little port of Salem came to boast that it had one of the finest scientific libraries in America.

Two members of the newly formed Philosophical Library Company—the Reverend Mr. Prince and the Reverend Mr. Bentley—were friends of Nat Bowditch. More than anyone else they understood his thirst for learning. They appreciated the lonely nights he spent studying and were sympathetic about his lack of books. They proposed and passed a resolution at a meeting of their group. It read that "Nathaniel Bowditch had the privilege of the Philosophical and Mathematic books of the library, to use them in the town of Salem only."

This was enough for Nat. Night after night he walked to the house of Reverend Prince and declared war on the Kirwan books. He only knew one way to study; he started on the top shelf and doggedly set sail for the last book on the bottom. It took him years!

Many of the books were written in French, but this was

no deterrent. Nat took time out from Kirwan to learn this language. He did it with a French grammar book and dictionary and methodically translated the entire New Testament. By the time he'd worked his way from the first verse of St. Matthew to the final "Amen" in Revelation, there was nothing in French in Richard Kirwan's library to stop him.

Another book which fell into Nat's hands during these years was *Philosophiae Naturalis Principia Mathematica.* This was the great work of the most magnificent thinker the world had yet produced—Sir Isaac Newton. *Principia Mathematica* was a precious mine for Nat Bowditch but as usual, in order to get at the information, he had to learn another language—this time Latin.

The *Principia* opened another world of pure thought for Nat. He grappled with problems and puzzled over solutions that have plagued the earth's finest minds—from the date of its publication in 1687 up to the present. Here was the whole universe put down in clear, concise, incredibly beautiful mathematical relationships. Calculus, the theories of gravitation and motion, the mathematics of light, the pull of the planets on each other, astronomy, telescopes—the majestic principles marched through his days and nights and sustained him in his dreary, dusty world of loneliness in the chandlery.

Nat was never content to take anybody's word for anything when it came to science. Not even Sir Isaac Newton's. Accordingly, as he plowed through the *Principia Mathematica,* he carefully checked every formula and mathematical conclusion. Late one weary evening, as his eyes were about to pop out of his head from strain, he sat bolt upright in his chair and felt a delicious thrill unlike any other he had ever known. Nat had discovered an error! He kept it to himself. Who was this young bookworm of an apprentice to go about boasting that he found a mistake in Newton's *Principia?*

Other books, too, began to come his way. The word was beginning to get around that there was a very odd bird clerking in a ship chandlery down in Salem, and occasionally people who had traveled, or who had even gone to Harvard, sent him mathematical works.

One such book was Euclid's *Elements,* a volume which posed various problems and theorems, which, when taken together, form the basis of modern geometry. Euclid lived about 500 B.C. during the reign of Ptolemy, a ruler of considerable knowledge. As Ptolemy puzzled over this new "science," he called Euclid to him and asked him if there was no way in which the study of geometry could be made any easier.

Euclid looked at the King and replied, "Sir, there is no royal road."

Like Ptolemy, Nat didn't find any royal road when he started studying Euclid. Here was the basic, raw stuff which far predated Newton. Here were the elements and principles of mathematics conceived in the very beginning, when the mind of man began to look outside of itself, outside of superstition, and tried to see clearly the mighty principles of natural laws.

The copy of the *Elements* over which Nat labored was in Latin, but he soon discovered that Euclid was speaking to him in a language far more universal. Euclid's words came across the centuries in the language of mathematics. Whether the book was in English, French, Latin, or any other tongue, came to mean very little. The basic tongue

[51]

was mathematics, and when Euclid spoke to him out of the past, Nat understood.

The years slid past, and finally Nat was twenty-one years old. Overnight his apprenticeship was ended. He was a free man. But free to do what? What was he to do in Salem and what could Salem do for him?

A tiny handful of men in the town, and even a few people in faraway Boston, recognized that Nat had probably the sharpest, the best mathematical mind in the entire United States. Most of the folk, however, had no idea at all of his real abilities, or of the distant realms of pure thought where his mind had been soaring. Their voyages were of a different kind, winding their slow way to far-off ports, across the long hills and valleys of the sea. These the sailors and merchants and shipowners could understand; of the far world's where Nat's mind had traveled, they had to remain in ignorance.

The people of Salem were aware of this. They were a little jealous, a little resentful, and more than a little irritated in the presence of this unaccountable young fellow who had so strangely bloomed in their workaday world. So a gap arose between him and his neighbors.

Nat did little to help lessen it. His disposition soured because of his unhappiness and frustration. He had spent his years in loneliness and in grinding study, educating himself in the highest areas of knowledge. Now when his apprenticeship was over, there seemed nothing for him to do but to continue selling salt pork and the like in the ship chandlery at wages so low he could scarcely keep alive on them. He was always hot-tempered, but his frustration and feeling of uselessness made him even sharper with people, more acid-tongued, more impatient with minds less gifted than his own.

Even physically, there was nothing about Nat Bowditch to command respect. He simply didn't grow. As an adult he was skinny, spindly. He never grew taller than five feet three or four inches. In a town where a big, powerful frame and physique were the rule, the only things big about Nat were his head and high, domed brow. And there were no rewards for these in Salem.

Salem folk didn't like Nat Bowditch very much, and he didn't like them. It was nobody's fault. The simple truth was that in the town there was no way for all his study and his knowledge to be put to use to help him earn a living. His predicament was driving him crazy and not endearing him in the least bit to his fellow townsmen. Worse, Nat could see no end to it. The future looked just as bleak as the present.

Nat did have friends, though, who recognized his genius, who appreciated his struggles and sympathized with him now, when he was at his wits' end to know what to do with himself. Two of these men came to his rescue.

One was an old and trusted mentor, the Reverend William Bentley of the Philosophical Library Company. The other was a figure out of the past, a shipmaster. He was Captain John Gibaut, the same sailorman who had had the terrible row with Elias Derby when his ship had been lost and then recaptured in the fight with pirates off Tripoli.

These two men—the spare, flinty preacher, clad in his somber black suit, and the portly, rolling captain—arrived one afternoon at the ship chandlery. They had a proposition for Nat.

[53]

The Commonwealth of Massachusetts had decreed that the time had come to make a survey of its lands and townships. Heretofore maps and property lines were largely a matter of by-guess and by-gosh. The legislators had decided that more accurate and permanent landmarks than barns, stones, a big bush or tree and so on, were in order.

Reverend Bentley and Captain Gibaut had been awarded a contract to survey the township of Salem and some of the surrounding countryside. They offered Nat the job of their assistant. He jumped at the chance. He didn't know anything about surveying, but angles and distances and straight lines between two points were an old, old story, and he was more than proud at this opportunity to put his unique knowledge to practical use.

The hills around Salem roll and toss and pitch gently down to the harbor as though they echoed the movement of the sea itself. These hills are very beautiful and were especially so this May of 1794, fair and smiling and blushing green under the soft winds and the sunshine of spring.

Nat, Reverend Bentley, and the captain relaxed on the crest of one of these hills, taking their ease and resting a moment from their labors. Below them were the buildings and the white spires of the town, and the tall masts of a few ships moored at the piers. Down the channel and beyond, the sea spread smooth and blue, as clear and shining and flawless as a gem.

A ship was making her landfall. Since early morning they had been observing her. First she had been only a black square of sail rising out of the sea beyond the horizon. Now she was nearer. Slowly she came up the channel into the harbor, a graceful queen, her white canvas swaying to and fro, bowing it seemed to her subjects, acknowledging their homage with regal grace.

"That'll be the *Indian Star*," murmured Gibaut. "John Horne, master."

Nat stared at her with emotion, but with resignation. He had long since given up any idea that the ships were for him. He was land-bound and knew it. Nevertheless, he could not look at a lovely square-rigger without a longing in his heart.

He had come to abhor the rough men who sailed the ships. They seemed brutal and ruthless, without any true awareness of the beauty and grace they commanded. But Nat did love the ships. He loved the marvelous logic and perfection which had gone so carefully into their construction. They were heavy and bulky and carried great weights and they were powerful, to do battle with the greatest seas and winds. At the same time they were dainty and delicate, moving like swans, with no more than the thin thrust of wind on canvas to give them life. There was nothing Nat wanted more than somehow to contribute something of his own to the magic he felt was woven into these beautiful creatures of the sea. His dreams were denied him; his eyes were bitter as he watched the *Indian Star*.

Captain Gibaut rumbled on. "She's deep. Fat with profit. The town'll celebrate tonight. The *Star*'s been gone a long time. Two years I think since she cleared Salem."

"Too long," snapped Nat. "Much too long."

"But she's been clear to the Indies," objected the captain. "That's a lengthy voyage, Mr. Bowditch."

Nat was irritated. He felt his temper rising, as it always did when this subject came up. "Allow for the distance. Allow for port delays, adverse winds, storms. Allow for everything you like, Captain Gibaut, and that still doesn't excuse the voyage taking that long."

"And what does explain it, Nat?" put in the Reverend Bentley. This was an old story to him; he liked to hear Nat sound off.

"She's been running in circles," said Nat. "Blind. The truth is she didn't know where she was on the ocean half the time."

"Now, now, that's too much, young man," said Captain Gibaut. "That ship's been navigated. I know John Horne very well. He's extremely capable."

Nat's voice, like the voices of many small men, rose when he was angry. "Navigation," he said. "You call what *he* does *navigation?* He's a blockhead, like all of 'em. Just pick a course on the compass, point the ship, and hope the good Lord doesn't give 'em a landfall on a dark night or in a fog. You call that *navigation?*"

Captain Gibaut was a fine, upright old man. What Nat said was partly true—true enough to make him squirm. He didn't answer for a moment, and then the sarcastic look on Nat's face touched off his own ire.

"And I suppose you could do better?" he asked.

Reverend Bentley stared innocently out over the bay and smothered a grin behind his hand.

"Yes. Yes I could," said Nat angrily. "Much better. Much better than these dolts that pass for navigators now. Ships should sail in a straight line and make passages the way they should be made, allowing for wind and weather. In a hurry."

[56]

"But . . . but . . ." sputtered the captain. "How would *you* do it?

Nat could no longer even try to be polite to the usually amiable old captain. "Listen," he cried. "It's just a matter of mathematics. Simple arithmetic. It never lies. On land or at sea."

"But men have tried," said Gibaut. "Many of them. And they have always come to grief. Listen, you landbound sailor, do you have any idea how many of these men you despise, and believe me, some of them have been mighty capable shipmasters, have lost their ships because they trusted arithmetic? I wish I could tell you."

"That's their fault," said Nat. "Not mathematics."

Captain Gibaut did not answer for a moment. When he finally spoke, his voice was calmer.

"All right, young man. Perhaps," he said. "But I still know something about it. And I know that to determine longitude, you've got to know the correct time. It's a matter of *time*. And no clock ever made will work on a tossing ship."

"There are other ways," said Nat.

"Moon sights? Lunar time sights?" asked Gibaut. He shook his head. "I know the theory. They're too involved for me."

"Well," said Nat, more calmly now also, "they've got clocks that'll work now. Keep good enough time if you have to have it. Buy a chronometer if you think it's so necessary."

Gibaut knew this. In 1775 a London clockmaker had invented a clock that would keep accurate time. But they were expensive, and, he wondered, even with this, could a man trust mathematics enough. *Really* trust it.

"Buy yourself a chronometer for your next voyage," prodded Nat, "if you can't do without one."

Gibaut started to flare again; Reverend Bentley concluded the argument had gone far enough. He rose to go back to work and the others followed him.

Several weeks later Captain Gibaut was in conference with Elias Hasket Derby, who had just appointed him as master of the small, but full-rigged ship *Henry*, for a voyage to the east coast of Africa. They were to sail shortly.

Derby looked at Gibaut and harumphed slightly. He had never fully trusted this captain since that unfortunate affair with the Tripoli pirates years before. "Still . . . still . . ." he thought to himself, "Gibaut was certainly an excellent man in all other respects."

Derby said, "Your principal cargo home will be coffee, Captain. And I must have a fast voyage. The *Henry* should be back in Salem in under a year in order to catch the coffee market at the top."

Gibaut had something on his mind. "Then let me make a suggestion, sir. Allow me to take a clerk."

Derby looked narrowly at Captain Gibaut. "And how will a clerk shorten the voyage, Captain? How will he pay his way?"

"By saving us time in port. To handle the ship's business. The accounting, the paying and receiving of money."

Derby grumbled under his breath. This possibly was true. But it still seemed a needless expense. Hiring a man to do the work the captain usually did? But still . . . he did want that fast voyage. "Where will you find such a man?"

"Nathaniel Bowditch, Mr. Derby. A young man of—"

"Yes, yes, I know of Mr. Bowditch," interrupted Derby. "I hear he has some small talent for numbers. Been keeping accounts for Ropes & Hodges."

"Indeed. Mr. Bowditch is mighty powerful in calculation."

Derby thought a moment, then made up his mind. "Very well. Sign Mr. Bowditch as ship's clerk. And second mate as well. See to it he stands a watch; under your supervision, of course. We cannot afford a man on board who does nothing but keep track of the cargo."

That afternoon Captain Gibaut left on a mysterious trip to Boston. He returned in two days and was immediately summoned to Derby's office.

Derby was apoplectic. He was wearing a bright scarlet waistcoat and its vivid color was pale compared to the hue of his neck and face.

Derby furiously waved a piece of paper at the captain. "And what is this, sir? What is this?" he roared.

Gibaut had no idea what the paper was.

"It's a note from a friend of mine in Boston. Reliable shipowner and a fine sailorman. And he informs me that one of my captains . . . *you*, sir, has just spent seven hundred dollars for a chronometer. Seven hundred dollars, sir. Have you gone mad?"

Captain Gibaut took out his handkerchief. It was silk, very large, and plum colored. He began to wipe his face, and a heavy sensation started to form in his stomach.

Derby said icily, "And what may I ask do you plan to use a chronometer for?"

Poor Captain Gibaut could only croak, "Find . . . longitude, sir."

[59]

"Longitude? *Longitude?*" roared Derby. "And what is wrong with determining your position the way my masters always do? They do it, sir, by being excellent sailors. That is how they do it, and that is how they will continue to do it."

Gibaut began to become a little riled himself at the injustice of this tirade. "I purchased the chronometer out of my own funds," he said.

"All the worse. I can only believe that your head has gone soft. Seven hundred of your hard-earned money for a contraption that can have no other result than the loss of *my* ship. What have you to say to this?"

Gibaut had nothing to say to this.

Derby had calmed down. He shook his head in exasperation. He looked at his captain. If only the man were not such a top-rate sailor. He'd fire him in a minute, and for good, but men as capable as Captain Gibaut were difficult to find.

Then he spoke. "I'll not permit such a thing on a ship of mine, Captain. Mechanical contrivances will never be allowed to supplant reliance on good sea sense on a Derby vessel. Consider yourself fortunate that I do not relieve you permanently. As it is, you are on the beach for two months. Perhaps this will be time enough for you to contemplate your error. The *Henry* will clear with someone else in command."

Five

When Captain Gibaut had offered Nat the opportunity to sail with him, his heart soared. The voyage seemed to open the door on the prospect of the whole wide world. When it slammed shut and the opportunity went glimmering, it seemed like the curtain of doom itself. Despair lay like a stone on his heart, with nothing but futility and frustration in view.

First things have to come first, though, and Nat didn't have much time to give way to his feelings. He had to keep on living, and this meant he had to have a job. He was nearly flat broke. Every penny he'd saved from the surveying job had been spent getting ready for the trip to sea.

He had spent some money buying suitable clothing for

the voyage. Most, however, he had invested in an "adventure."

Except for some of the common hands in the foc'sle, almost everyone those days who sailed on a windjammer undertook what was called an adventure. An adventure was a small business transaction, an attempt to pick up a little extra money on a voyage. It consisted in buying a bit of merchandise of some kind, stowing it in a seabag, a locker, or under a bunk, and hoping that the goods could be sold at a profit in some foreign port. This money would then be reinvested in goods in that port—perhaps a picul of pepper, a box of tea, a bolt of silk or satin, or some other such thing, which could be disposed of at a profit back in America. Often, even people who did not go to sea could persuade an officer or someone else on a ship to conduct some such small enterprise for them. It was an excellent way for people with very limited means to invest their money and so accumulate capital enough to get into something bigger.

The practice was condoned, even encouraged, by owners and masters. Wages for sailors were extremely low—the captain himself on a good-sized ship might, if he were lucky, be paid forty or fifty a month—and the opportunity to pick up extra money on an adventure kept everyone more content.

Nat's adventure outbound was to have consisted of a box of shoes, for which he had paid twelve dollars. With luck he could double or treble this money, and do the same with whatever he decided to buy to bring home with him. When the trip fell through, he sadly piled the now useless shoes and his new clothing in his room and went back to work in the chandlery.

The time passed very slowly. Matters did not go well for Nat as a sort of "super-apprentice." He was tired and despairing. His mind was trained superbly in mathematics, and the frustration of selling salt pork and the like in the chandlery was too much.

Several weeks went by. Down at one end of the counter he had once again set up a sort of workshop with the tools of his seemingly useless profession. Here, when he was not waiting on customers, among the devices for measuring angles, a sphere, charts of the heavens, and so on, he scribbled calculations on a slate. The *Henry* had not yet sailed; he could see the tips of her masts rising up above the warehouse, and every time he looked at them, he fumed, his ire increasing.

The weather that winter of 1794 was miserable, and his irritability increased in direct proportion to it. Furthermore, he had gone all out now for his cause of celestial navigation and he beat the drums for it at every opportunity. He was absolutely convinced that the only reliable way to take a ship to sea and bring her home safely in the least possible time was to steer her by the stars.

If Nat believed this, nobody else did! The steady stream of customers who came to the chandlery—the mates and masters—stood up for what they believed and invariably became the objects of Nat's temper, his withering scorn. These sailormen followed the methods that seamen had used for centuries. Seamanship and sea sense alone took them out and brought them home. They were not about to change their minds because of something that Nathaniel Bowditch said. To them he was a snappish little land-bound bookkeeper with no idea of the problems which they had to face when they took a ship to sea. Some of these worthies became highly furious at Nat's insistence. Some laughed at him; others tried to explain why celestial navigation wouldn't work.

Whatever their reaction to his impassioned arguments, they were as apt as not to end up being called thick-skulled dolts. This did not increase Nat's popularity in the town. He became the butt of many a joke, scorned and laughed at, and the nickname he was called in frequent derision was the Arithmetic Sailor.

One afternoon early in January 1795, Nat had finished waiting on a customer, the captain of a Boston ship which happened to be in port. After a long, long trip the man had brought his vessel into Salem for refuge in the face of a bitter storm before beating his way up the coast to his home port.

His business in the chandlery finished, the mariner stood chatting a moment with the clerk. He was glad to tell somebody about his troubles on the trip. It had been very, very long. The ship had been out nearly three years, trading through the East Indies and along the China coast.

Nat was curious as to the length of the voyage. "Lots of bad weather," he asked.

"The usual. No more than normal, I suppose. Main reason was that we missed the monsoon homeward bound. Had to wait out six months on Sumatra for the shift."

"Why didn't you head into the monsoon?" asked Nat.

"What?" The honest captain was scandalized. "You don't know how it is amongst those islands. Never been to sea, I take it. A ship's got to have the fair wind. Don't dare take a chance in that part of the world without it."

[64]

"What you really mean," said Nat sourly, "is that you don't dare take the chance because you never know exactly where you are."

"I suppose that's it," the captain said mildly. He wasn't looking for an argument. "You never know your exact position. If you'd ever been to sea you'd know how it is."

"Don't have to go to sea. All you've got to do is navigate your ship properly."

"Now see here, young fellow . . ." The captain's temper was rising. "I'm as good a navigator as you'll find."

"Don't doubt it," snapped Nat. "And that's not very good."

"And you could do better? How?"

"By the stars. The unvarying stars. They'll tell you where you are if you've got sense enough to let them."

"By gads, sir. I've a notion to report you to the owner of this place. Of all the impertinent . . ." The captain picked up his purchases. He was in no mood to argue any more with this skinny little clerk. He started for the door. Nat followed, unable to break off the argument, talking in a loud voice about the marvels which would take place if only sailors would navigate by arithmetic instead of by the seat of their pants.

The fuming mariner finally made good his escape. Nat returned to the counter, pale with fury, muttering angrily to himself. He hadn't noticed another man, who was standing off to one side and who had been watching the show with an amused grin.

"Dolt. Fool," sputtered Nat. "Any idiot knows a straight line's the shortest distance between two points. These people *like* to sail in circles."

"That's right, Nat," said the other man.

Nat whirled at something in the voice. In a second all his anger was gone. His face broke into a big grin. "Henry, Henry Prince," he said.

It was indeed Henry Prince, old friend of Nat's boyhood. Henry had been gone a long time. The two hadn't seen each other for years. Prince had been a Captain a long time, and now, at thirty-one, was regarded as one of the best masters in Elias Derby's fleet. He had the same old devil-may-care look of no-nonsense in his eyes that Nat remembered. As he gazed at the peppery, impatient little man into whom his boyhood friend had grown, these wide blue eyes broke into a broad glow of affection.

"Nat," said Prince, after consulting a huge, expensive-looking watch, "close up shop. It's late. Let's walk a bit before I go to my rooms. Tell me about yourself."

In a few moments Nat and Prince were strolling through the streets of the town, headed for the waterfront. In Salem, whenever people took a short stroll, there was but one place to go: the docks.

They passed Derby wharf. The *Henry* was in port. She'd been re-outfitted for sea, and with her new rigging and neatly furled white sails, she looked clean and fresh and ready to go, impatient to be out on the ocean where she belonged.

The two men paused to look at her. In Prince's eyes, there was cool, professional speculation; in Nat's, dreary despair.

Prince laughed shortly. He knew the story. "Poor Captain Gibaut. Finally got it from old Derby. And all over a chronometer, I understand."

Nat nodded. "Yes. And I got it too. I was to sail in her, you know."

This did surprise Prince. "You?"

Nat flared. "Yes. Me. Why not? Maybe I'm not a big mass of muscles, but I can still pull my weight."

Prince backed off, laughing. "Now, now, Nat. Don't get so hot. After all, we've just gotten together after a good many years."

Nat was contrite. "Of course. Forgive me. And I was only going as clerk. Derby's beginning to put 'em on his ships to do the paper work."

"So I hear, so I hear," said Prince. Then, "Nat, did Gibaut really get the sack over a chronometer?"

"That's the rumor."

"And I wonder," mused Prince, "I wonder why Gibaut would want a chronometer?"

"Because he's a smart man. He's tired of running his ship around half blind," said Nat. "Anyhow, look at the *Henry*. She's a small ship. Only way she could be made to earn her way in is fast voyages. And how else can you make 'em but sailing in a straight line?"

"Hmmm," said Prince. The ship was small. Heavy weather would certainly slow her down. If she could be navigated accurately it undoubtedly would save time. "Nat," he said. "Tell me the truth. Can a course *really* be plotted accurately . . . and a position fixed . . . by arithmetic? Safely?"

By now Nat was tired arguing. He'd had about enough for one day. "Look, Henry," he said wearily, "I know mathematics. I believe in it. It does not lie. Ashore or at sea. Mathematics is truth."

Prince nodded. Something in the earnest humility of his old friend caught his imagination.

Nat continued. He was an honest man; with Prince

there was no point in exaggerating. He said, "I've never been to sea. Theoretically it'll work. On a ship there'll be problems. Maybe too great to surmount. But I don't think so. I'll say it again: I believe in mathematics and I believe in the steadfast paths of the stars. They do not change, and if only man will use this constancy, and trust it, then certainly, some day, celestial navigation will work. It has to."

"Nat," said Prince, "a good many fine sailors have lost their ships with it. They weren't all dolts."

Nat faced this squarely. "I know," he said. "Sometimes I fly off the handle, but I know what you're saying is true. But I can't help believe that it was they who failed. Not mathematics. If I could make a trip to sea I'm sure I could work out methods that would be reliable."

For a long moment, Prince said nothing. Then, "Captain Gibaut must have thought that too. Was that why you were going with him?"

Nat hesitated. Truthfully, he didn't know the answer, and in any event, he was not about to say anything that might trouble Captain Gibaut more. "I don't know," he said. "But someday men *will* plot courses for their ships by the stars. And make passages in half the time."

There was no sound but the usual lap of water along the piers, the cry of an occasional gull, and the rumbling screech of the fenders of the moored vessel as she surged back and forth on her lines and rubbed the dock.

"Is a chronometer necessary?" finally asked Prince.

Nat was sure about this. "No. They're too expensive, and even the newest ones don't keep time accurately enough. Good maybe for short voyages but not for crossing an ocean."

[68]

"And how would you do it? You must know the time if you're to calculate longitude. Use lunar sights? Men have been trying to take lunar time sights for hundreds of years without much luck."

"I know that too," said Nat. "But there has to be a way. The moon's speed and its orbit are constant. They can be predicated. Accurately. There's got to be a proper way of finding time with lunar sights."

Night was falling now. The two friends—irascible little Nathaniel Bowditch, the Arithmetic Sailor, and beside him, swinging easily in his long sailor's roll, Captain Prince—returned to town. They parted—Prince to go to a tavern for a convivial glass or two with shipmaster friends, and Nat to go to his room to ponder.

Elias Hasket Derby's office was on the second floor of the big warehouse hard by the wharf. The stairway was narrow, and twisting and dark and it was redolent with odors and fragrances of cargoes from half the world. The smell of the sea, of tar, of wet hemp and of the ships themselves mixed in a heavy aroma with that of coffee, leather, pepper, nutmeg, cinnamon, molasses, rum, and much more.

Captain Henry Prince was a young man and very light on his feet, but he was also six feet of solid muscle and bone. The steps on the stairway creaked as he tramped up them. They were more accustomed to the lighter weight and gentler tread of bookkeepers.

He reached the top, turned into Derby's outer office. It was like all business establishments of the day. Back of a rail fence long rows of clerks industriously scratched away with their quill pens. They didn't dare stop for a moment, for if they had, the wrath of the chief accountant would have descended on their thin shoulders like a blast from the Good Lord Himself. So, back of the rail—nobody could have said why a rail was necessary to fence off such harmless men—they stayed grimly at their work, keeping track of the endless cargoes and tallying up Elias Derby's profits.

Prince paused briefly at the rail and instantly the chief accountant came to him.

"Good afternoon, Captain," he said. "Mr. Derby is expecting you. Please follow me."

Prince had been to this inner sanctum many times before, but he followed along obediently. The protocol was that he should be formally announced by the clerk. He stepped inside and stood waiting respectfully, still keeping the custom. Prince was a master mariner, Derby's most trusted captain and the equal of any man on earth, but established manners between him and Derby demanded a certain conduct from each of them.

He bowed formally. "Good afternoon, sir," he said.

Derby also obeyed the rules. He rose to his feet and bowed. "Good afternoon, Captain."

The formalities over, Derby smiled his wintry little smile and indicated a chair for Prince. He liked this tall and muscular young captain. Prince was daring: he'd take a ship where other men would not trust to go. And he'd get her out, too. He drove a ship hard, the way they should be driven. He made fast voyages, he took care of his men —there were few widows and orphans made on a vessel Prince commanded. Derby also liked the glint in Prince's eyes. To Derby this glint gleamed like a bright pair of

dollar signs. Prince liked money; his voyages were profitable ones, something to delight any shipowner.

Their business was already nearly settled. Prince was
to take out the *Henry*. She was small—Prince would have
liked something bigger perhaps but it didn't really matter.
He was on his way to being a shipowner himself, and a
few more voyages in Derby ships were all he needed. The
Henry was perfectly all right with him. She was loaded
and ready for sea. Tomorrow the iron strongbox, filled with
glittering gold coins, would be taken aboard. A shipmaster
in those days was not only a sailor, but was a representative
of the owner, empowered to buy and sell and go where he
pleased, as long as he made money. He was out of contact
with his owner for months on end, sometimes years. He
had to be a man who was trusted—and Prince was such.

There was but one small matter yet to be settled. Prince
had it on his mind and was about to speak, when Derby
brought up the subject.

"Mr. Prince, I've decided on a new policy. My ships will
now sail with clerks to take care of the vessel's business.
Under the master's supervision, of course."

"Yes, sir," said Prince. "I believe it a good idea."

"Well . . . I don't know. A luxury perhaps. But I feel
that you captains will be at a greater advantage to the
ship and voyage in general if relieved of the paper work."

"I quite agree, sir," said Prince."

"The first one was to have gone with Captain Gibaut
until that master went quite soft in the head and bought
a chronometer."

Prince clucked in understanding.

"I'll not have such contraptions on any ship of mine,
Captain. Only sailors will take them out and bring them

home. Seafaring men. Not springs and gears. Do you agree?"

"Oh yes, quite, sir," said Prince innocently. "A chronometer is quite an unreliable instrument. Most expensive, too."

"Good. Good."

"Who do you have in mind, Mr. Derby?"

"I intend to engage Mr. Nathaniel Bowditch of this town. If he is at liberty. Do you know him, Captain? And is this agreeable to you?"

Prince could not have been more pleased, but he didn't show it. "Oh yes," he said. "Mr. Bowditch is quite satisfactory. Capable with numbers too, I understand."

"Very good. And be sure to sign him as second mate. Can't afford clerks who do nothing but scribble manifests. He'll have to take his share of the ship's work."

"Right, sir," said Prince, but he hid a smile behind his hand. In his mind's eye he saw Nat, bundled and half hidden in oilskins, pacing the poop deck in a gale.

"And now, sir, that this is settled, let us drink to the voyage." Derby hoisted a gout-swollen foot from where it had been resting on a stool, and put it gingerly on the floor. Grunting and swearing, he hobbled to the sideboard, picked out a tall bottle of wine and two tiny cut-crystal glasses.

He returned to his chair, still swearing at his misery. "Damme. Damme. Oh, bless my soul," he groaned. He hoisted the painful foot back on the stool, gave out with a huge grunt of relief. "Whew, sir," he said, wiping his face with his handkerchief. "May the good Lord grant you never have the gout. Most miserable."

They solemnly toasted the voyage, and each other, in

minute little glasses of Madeira wine. In a few moments, Prince was gone, trailing the aroma of good Havana cigars and vintage port behind him, to the envy of the clerks in the counting room. If they paused to sniff too long, the head accountant rapped sharply on his desk with his ruler to bring them back to their senses.

Derby limped to the window of his office and watched the broad, lithe figure swing up the wharf and head into the town. His eyes were wistful. He too was envious of the arrogant young strength of his captain.

Six

Captain Prince immediately passed by the chandlery to give Nat the news.

Nat was "at liberty" and needed only a few minutes to tell his employers he was no longer their man. Truthfully, they might have been even a bit relieved. Nat had been too insulting to some of their best customers over the business of celestial navigation.

The Arithmetic Sailor's spirits soared. His natural cheerfulness asserted itself. He was walking on air. He was going to sea for sure, at last. In his imagination, nothing now seemed out of reach or impossible. The doldrums and the hopelessness of life in Salem were to be left behind for good, forever. Money, security, respect, adventure—all awaited him now.

He also hugged another cherished hope to his heart.

Henry Prince was an old friend; he hoped he was a good enough friend and broad-minded enough to allow him to experiment with celestial navigation. Nat buried this dream stealthily in his heart and said nothing, but he made very sure that his notebooks and his reference books were carefully included in his sea chest. He repacked all his seagoing clothes once again, as well as the box of shoes for his adventure. As he dusted them off he dreamed a dream of soaring profits from them.

Everything was taken down to the *Henry*. In Nat's capacity as an officer, even a quasi-officer, he now had a dignity to maintain, so he spent nearly his last penny to hire a roustabout to carry the bags and boxes to the ship and stow them properly in the tiny cabin off the main saloon which would be his home for many months to come.

Then he settled down with the accountants in Derby's warehouse. The helter-skelter method of keeping track of all the merchandise which had been sent into the gaping holds of the ship offended his sense of order and precision. As far as he was concerned, the cargo and the quantities should all be symbolized by numbers and numbers must always be neat and tidy. When Nat was done going over the manifests, he knew exactly what was on the ship, where it was stowed, and its value. Safe to say that few ships had ever left Salem with as thorough and useful a set of papers.

Captain Prince was exceedingly pleased to be relieved of this tedious detail work. He and Derby congratulated each other on the businesslike way in which Nat completed the job.

At last everything was aboard. The hatches were battened down, tarpaulins spread over them, and secured. The crew was aboard, and the *Henry* was ready for sea.

Salem shipowners and merchants believed in small ships. Disasters were so common at sea that they preferred not to put all their eggs in one basket. They reasoned that it was more prudent to divide them among several smaller ones. Even by these conservative standards, however, the *Henry* was a small ship, although strong, honestly built and rigged. Because of her size, Prince had delayed leaving port.

For days the town had been smothered in the grip of a winter blizzard. By the eleventh of January, 1795, the storm showed signs of having spent its power. The enormous black seas seemed to have lost some of their authority as they crashed on the rocky coast. The sky was a shade lighter and the driving snow squalls had thinned.

Captain Prince fumed. He hated to stay in port just because it was blowing a bit outside. He was not the man to remain sheltered at home when he had a good ship under him, loaded, manned, and ready to go. Neither voyages nor money were made this way.

In spite of his impatience, though, Prince was no fool. Intimate association with the sea over many years had taught him great respect for it. The ocean could be a benign, tranquil friend; it could also be a devastating and ferocious enemy.

On the morning of the eleventh, he stood in the main cabin of the *Henry*. Even though the storm was still howling, some sixth sense told him that its strength was dwindling, that the weather would be clearing. Aft, through the open companionway at the top of the ladder which led

from the saloon to the poop he could catch a glimpse of
the sky. The clouds were still streaked and torn as they
raced overhead, and even tied to a sheltered dock as she
was, the *Henry* stirred and moved uneasily in response to
that greater movement which wracked the ocean outside
the channel. The storm was not over yet.

For the hundredth time in the last few days, Prince
checked his barometer. Its old-fashioned, long brass case
swung gently in the gimbals. The captain was well aware
of the tried and true seafaring adage: "Never put to sea
with a falling barometer," and he had no intention of
violating the rule. Now, though, it seemed to him that the
barometer, which had been low, was beginning to fluctu-
ate a bit, starting to rise. He was sure of it. The atmos-
pheric pressure was commencing to go up; this meant
that the winds would stop pouring into the area. The
weather had to clear, no matter what it seemed like now.
The turn had been reached. The column of mercury did
not lie. It was a faithful servant and foretold the future
accurately. Prince made up his mind and went up the
ladder.

He gave an order to the man on watch and quickly the
cry went through the ship. "All hands. All hands!" With
a rush, the crew came tumbling out of the foc'sle.

Getting the square-rigger under way and putting to sea
was really quite a simple matter in spite of the complexity of the sails.

The dock was deserted because of the weather, but a
bellow from the mate, who, among his other excellent
qualities, had a tremendously powerful voice, brought a
handful of roustabouts from the warehouse. They stood by
the lines on the big mooring bits.

[77]

Prince spoke quietly to the mate. Another roar from him and the sailors were standing by braces and jib halyards.

Another order and the cry to the dock. "Let go. Let go!"

The people ashore took the lines from the bits and tossed them into the water. The men on the *Henry* quickly hauled them aboard. The ship floated free.

Still another order. With a banshee squealing of blocks and pulleys, the jib went fluttering up the forestay. It banged and thundered violently a moment in the heavy wind and then fell utterly silent, bellied out and pulling strongly.

The *Henry* began to move ahead very slowly. The helm was put over and with the press of wind on the jib, the bow commenced to turn, working away from the dock. Gradually the ship turned until the dock was astern and she was headed down the channel.

Prince sent the men into the rigging now to set reefed topsails on all the masts, then the crew on deck braced the yards around to the right angle so the sails would catch the wind. The canvas ceased its thunderous banging and flapping and began to draw. The *Henry* heeled slightly, moving ever more quickly, with the water beginning to hiss and gurgle beneath her bow, along her sides and under the stern.

On the port tack, with the wind coming over the left side, she continued to pick up speed and began a gliding rush down the smooth harbor water of the channel to the open sea. This was the moment of the magic of sail. The ship, deep and heavy with cargo, slid over the water without a tremor, a quiver, or the slightest sound except that of the wind. No fumes, no thud of propeller, no clatter and clank of machinery. A steamship eternally seems an alien on the sea; a sailing vessel seems a part of it, as much a part as a soaring gull.

Elias Derby pulled back the curtains on his office window and watched the *Henry* head to sea. The departure of the ship had been strictly up to her captain; he would never interfere in such a matter, but he loved to see his ships on their way, storm or no storm. He nodded to himself in approval of Captain Prince.

To those on the *Henry*, Salem was quickly lost in the gloom astern. Then she passed the open meadows and pastures of Marblehead, dim in the murk. Next the town of Beverly was gone, and finally the glimmer of Baker Light was left behind. The little wooden ship was at last alone, with only the vast Atlantic for company.

The wind was stronger now that the vessel was completely clear of the land. Prince reduced sail even more; already the *Henry* had begun to ship green water. Under the shortened sail she settled down more easily to the long, tumbling path ahead.

Nat had seen many ships leave port; this was the first time he had been on one, and there was a vast difference. He observed the ocean and marveled. The giant rollers, the enormous graybeards over which the ship climbed, raced down upon her in a never-ending procession. At their crests the wild waves spread in all directions as far as he could see. From the bottoms of the deep black valleys between, nothing could be seen except the next monstrous wave bearing down on the vessel.

Nat marveled too at the consummate skill with which Prince had set precisely the amount of sail to keep the ship at her business and yet not to force her. She submitted easily to the press of the canvas, didn't fight the seas, but seem to settle down, become one with the ocean. She snuggled down into it, weather rail thundering, lee rail hissing, and seemed to say, "Here I am, wild ocean. There's only you and me. I know you won't hurt me; just give me passage." And so it was.

The sail and course were finally set exactly as Prince wanted. The mate busied the crew stowing the lines and other gear left from the stay in port. Then he went below to get some rest before watch time.

Nat also went below and donned his brand-new creaky oilskins. He peered out like a worried little mouse from beneath his huge sou'wester hat. This was his watch as second mate, and he expected to stand it properly. Already he was a bit humbled; there was more to sailing a square-rigged ship than he'd thought.

When he returned to the poop deck he was relieved to see that Prince was still there, talking with the seaman at the wheel. He said to Nat, "Just see she keeps her compass course, Nat. And don't worry. The wind'll go down and so will the sea. Be sure the lookout stays awake."

Nat nodded but Prince continued. He gestured at the man steadying the big wheel. "Let old Jack here manage the rest. He knows more about handling this ship than anybody aboard her. Call me if you need anything."

Nat looked at the grinning, weather-seamed face of the old man. It was dimly aglow in the light coming from the compass lamp. Suddenly Nat was full of questions and he started to spill them out to Prince, when, all in a moment, like the clap of doom itself, his stomach did an absolute turn-over. Devastating cramps and waves of nausea poured over him. He scuttled to the rail, thanking his stars he'd headed to the lee. He was as seasick as any man had ever been.

Prince looked at the helmsman, and the man looked back at the captain. A very small ghost of a smile flitted across each face. It would never do for a foremast hand and the captain to exchange words or make a joke about the plight of the second officer. To keep from laughing outright, though, Prince had to turn his back and stare far out over the sea. This was something he hadn't anticipated; it had been a good many years since he'd been reminded that people got seasick. Back turned, Prince grinned at the hissing black seas.

As for the Arithmetic Sailor, he hung weakly on the lee rail and very quickly wished he was dead. Everything else in the world but his own misery was forgotten. Of the majesty of the paths of the stars, the beauty of mathematics, and the precision of celestial navigation, he wanted nothing.

Before Captain Prince went below he paused to throw a long, professional glance at his ship and aloft at his masts and the straining scraps of sails. The canvas was full, tightly swelling. The rigging was taut, each line taking its proper share of the load of power which was pulling the ship through the water. Each line too, according to its size and shape, vibrated and sang as the wind passed by it. The howl of the air pouring past each of these lines produced a mass bedlam, a deep thrumming, deafening roar. Prince cocked his head, listening. He found nothing to disturb him. It was the sweet sound of a gale wind in a strong ship.

Then he looked forward along the deck, past the watch

huddled in the lee of the galley for protection. The *Henry* was racing over the wild seas in long shuddering swoops, but again, he was satisfied. She was working hard but that was good. She was designed to work. She was well within her limits of strength and would keep at her job without complaint.

Prince walked now across the heaving poop and checked the binnacle. In the light of the whale-oil lamp, the compass card pointed true and steady and the ship was on her course. He spoke briefly to the helmsman then walked below to the cabin.

There was no sound in the cabin except the normal racket of a working ship. He listened intently a moment to the squeaks and groans of her straining timbers. Nothing was amiss. Going to a locker, he took out his chart of the broad Atlantic and spread it out on the table.

Quietly Prince smoothed out the chart, and by the light of the oil lamp swinging from the overhead, he settled in a chair and applied his mind to the navigation problems of the long voyage ahead. In dedicated silence, Prince kept his faith with the sea and all those others who had entrusted their ships and their lives upon it over the centuries.

In 1795, as Captain Henry Prince sat in the cabin of his ship, much had been accomplished to help guide him to his destination. The methods and the calculations which he would have to use were exceedingly complex and difficult. They were so difficult in fact that they were beyond the abilities of most of the simple seamen who trod the decks of merchant and navy ships of the times. These used those principles of astronomy that they could understand, but relied primarily on traditional rule of thumb, a quick glance at sea and star and wind, and their own common instincts.

Prince, however, was an exceptionally skilled mariner and navigator. There was little he didn't know about his business. His ship was well equipped with an excellent compass, the best charts available, and a good sextant. He could locate his position north and south of the Equator with considerable difficulty but still with considerable accuracy. But this was only half the battle.

Even Prince was completely stopped by one aspect of navigation which had as yet not been solved. He had no way to know where he was accurately in an east-west position.

Prince sat looking at his chart, seeing in his mind the long, long run into the South Atlantic, the groping passage to the east around the Cape of Good Hope, northward again to Madagascar and at last the destination still farther east, the island of Bourbon. He shook his head in frustration. The route could be much shorter, more direct, but he didn't dare risk the safety of his ship. He couldn't sail in a direct line without knowing exactly where he was every moment. And he had no way to know.

Prince drummed a pencil on the chart in frustration. He threw a quick glance upward to where Nat Bowditch on the poop deck was apparently retching his life out on the lee rail, and grunted in impatience. He wished Nat would get his sea legs. It just might be that the answer to the problem lay buried in the big, domed head of Salem's Arithmetic Sailor. Prince meant to find out.

He finished what calculations he could and plotted a course to the south. Then he rolled up the chart, stowed it, and went to his cabin. From his private supply he took a small, quick drop of rum to fortify himself against the wind and cold topside. He'd be up most of the night, he knew. Nat was in no condition to stand a watch, even if he had known how.

From the poop the wake of the ship gleamed whitely as she tore along. Overhead the sky was clearing a bit. An occasional star swam serenely in the blackness revealed in patches shredded from the clouds by the wind.

Seven

When Captain Prince sat in his cabin the night the *Henry* cleared Salem and puzzled out his course for the ship, he faced squarely the dilemma that every other mariner in the world had to confront. What course could he plot and follow safely in the light of the skills and knowledge available to him?

The first and longest leg of the passage was from Salem down through the Atlantic, to the Cape of Good Hope at the southern tip of Africa. To get there he had two choices, and both of them were bad. Each was the "long way around" by many, many miles and would eat up weeks, perhaps months, of precious extra time. Each had its own built-in and very real set of dangers. The entire trouble was that he would never know exactly where he was in an east-west position.

Here was what he faced:

He could sail the *Henry* due east, with a little southing for luck, until he picked up the coastline of Europe or Africa, praying that he wouldn't make his landfall on a dark or stormy night when the chances of being driven ashore as he groped for the land were excellent. He then would turn south, wind and weather permitting, and creep and blunder down the entire west coast of Africa to Capetown, more or less in sight of the coast the whole time, and following mainly the track of the muddy yellow silt of Africa's great rivers as they poured into the sea.

This was by far the most dangerous of the two choices and would only be taken by a captain who had been blown far off his course or, what was more likely, was such an inept navigator, that he felt continually uneasy unless he were in sight of land. Many and many a ship, however, had made her fumbling run to the Indies via this route.

Prince's second choice was to head far enough east to be sure he was clear of the land in the West Indies and the coast of South America, then turn to the starboard and head due south. He would then, in the time-honored phrase of sailing ships, "run down his latitude" until he picked up the roaring forties and in his judgment was about due west of the Cape of Good Hope. Here he would turn to the port and steer due east, plotting a course as carefully as he could by dead reckoning. (This doesn't mean "dead" but comes from *dedu*ced reckoning. It means distances and positions which the captain would deduce from many sources—all of them rough—such as speed through the water, wind strength, a little astronomy, and so on.)

As a ship steering such a course began to approach the

vicinity of the Cape, the nerves of all hands would tighten. Extra lookouts would be posted, extra care taken during dark nights. She *had* to find the Cape of Good Hope!

This seems such a simple thing to modern mariners, but when Captain Prince took the *Henry* to sea, it was far from being so. The peril was enormous; it gave captains gray hairs and kept them on deck night after night. If the ship were too far north, she could pound ashore on the coast of Africa. If she were too far south she could miss the Cape entirely, and spend weeks beating about in the southern Indian Ocean trying to work her way back to it. And find it she must, for the Cape of Good Hope was the departure point for vessels bound to the Indies.

Both of these mishaps—running ashore, or missing the Cape—had overtaken more than one good ship because there was no reliable method of determining east-west positions, positions that is, in *longitude*. Nevertheless, this was the course Prince had decided upon. He was an excellent navigator, better than many of the day, and could take star altitudes with enough accuracy to give him trustworthy fixes in latitude. As for the crucial computations, those for determining longitude, he was helpless. But he set the course to run down his latitude, giving it a bit of easting to save time and hoping that his terribly seasick second mate could be of help. Otherwise, he'd do as he had done many times before, sail his ship east by the seat of his pants.

The problem of the determination of longitude had bedeviled sailors from the very first moment they undertook voyages out of sight of land. For thousands of years mariners, astronomers, and mathematicians had tried in vain to invent a way in which it could be done. The steady sweep of the stars seemed to beckon and to offer the promise of an easy solution, but it had eluded everyone.

By 1795, when Prince and Bowditch took the *Henry* to sea, the problem had become acute. Europe's great powers were expanding overseas at a great rate. Their navies were dividing the world into far-flung empires. Ships were bigger and safer and could transport more cargo. Industry was clamoring for raw materials, and backward lands needed the goods of Europe's factories. Everything was ready and waiting. Ships that got to their destinations in the least time with the most cargo could reap fabulous fortunes for their owners and crews, and secure rich colonies for their homelands. There was little that could be done, however, until men knew how to navigate properly. Voyages stretched out interminably, to everyone's loss.

For centuries the great maritime powers had offered fantastic rewards to the man who could devise a way to lick the problem of determining longitude. France, Holland, Spain, Portugal offered fat cash prizes for the solution. Even Great Britain, the mighty mistress of the seas, established a permanent Board of Longitude to grapple with the problem. These rewards totaled more than a million dollars.

Thousands of years before this time, the path toward a solution had been pointed out. A Greek scholar and astronomer suggested that just as imaginary lines of latitude had been drawn around the earth, with the distance between two degrees equal to about sixty-nine miles, so should be done with longitude.

These lines of longitude, or *meridians*, as they were called, would converge at each Pole. The distance between two degrees at the Equator was, like that of latitude, about sixty-nine miles, but because the lines converged, the closer a ship got to the North or South Pole, the shorter this distance became. Right at a Pole, the distance would be zero, because the lines all came together.

Thus it was that for a long, long time, the surface of our globe had been broken up into an imaginary grid of lines—parallel lines representing latitude and, at right angles to them, converging lines or meridians representing longitude. The trouble was that only the parallels of latitude were really useful. Mariners looked at the longitude meridians in frustration; they knew *what* to do but they didn't know *how* to do it. Nevertheless, the solution came closer.

The first big step took place when an astronomer was able to measure the speed of the rotation of the earth. He noted that it revolved through 15 degrees of longitude *every hour!* Now they were getting somewhere. They knew how far it was between degrees of longitude, starting with sixty-nine miles at the Equator, so the reasoning was correct: so much time difference between a ship's location and some previously agreed upon fixed point could be expressed as degrees, minutes, and seconds, or as miles, and pricked off on a chart! The trouble with this, as mariners quickly found out, was that the calculations had to be made for the same, exact moment of time of the ship's position and that of the fixed point.

And here the problems really began.

First of all, the fixed point had to be settled upon and used by all ships of all nations. Every country wanted this point, or the *prime meridian* as it was to be called, to run through a big port of their own, or perhaps even the capital of their nation. One prime meridian was established which ran through Cadiz, in Spain. Another went through Paris. Eventually, though, when the squabbling was over, all countries accepted that meridian which ran through the Royal Observatory in Greenwich, England.

Greenwich Observatory is still used. It was established in 1675 by Charles the Second of England for the express purpose of observing the paths of the stars. Hopefully, the mathematicians and astronomers would work out a method to allow England's naval and merchant ships to move more swiftly and accurately about the earth. Greenwich is the zero point, the starting point for all time, and hence all longitude, on the globe. The 360 degrees around the circle of the earth are divided into two halves of 180 degrees each, going outward from Greenwich, one east and the other west.

The idea was simple and brilliant. The answer to the vexing problem of longitude seemed at hand. Imagine a ship somewhere in the middle of the Atlantic. The captain knew his position was in *west longitude*. Instruments and techniques had been developed so he could determine the exact time, or local time as it was called, at his ship's position. Remembering that in *one hour* the globe spins through 15 degrees of longitude, all he had to do was to compare the difference between his time, and that back in Greenwich, and then plot off his position on the meridians on his chart.

But there was a catch, and a bad one. The hang-up was to know the exact time in Greenwich! The solution seemed simple. Build a good watch, set it to Greenwich time on leaving port, and carry it with the ship on all her travels.

It wasn't simple, though, and centuries were to pass before the answer was found.

The trouble was that in those days no timepiece could be made that was accurate enough. Hour glasses were no good. Water glasses, pendulum clocks, spring clocks— all were tried and could not be trusted at all. Even ashore, clocks did not run accurately, and on a pitching ship, running through every conceivable variation in weather and temperature, they were absolutely useless.

For several centuries, lunar sights were considered to offer the most promising answer to the dilemma. Through observations made on the moon and calculation of the angles it made with other planets and stars, it was hoped that the time *back* at the prime meridian could be determined on a ship thousands and thousands of miles distant. This was the main function of the Greenwich observatory: to calculate accurately and to provide tables of the future positions of the moon and the stars to be used in the sights.

Lunar sights didn't work very well. In theory the principle was sound, but in practice it was something else. It was far too complicated. The sights were enormously difficult to make accurately, and, in addition, the mathematics of astronomy—spherical trigonometry and calculus among them—were simply out of the question for the simple mariners who had to use them.

So the problem of longitude remained, only now it was defined: how to tell Greenwich time on a ship halfway around the world from the observatory. Radios and international time signals do the trick today, but in those days there was nothing. As the rewards mounted, the schemes grew increasingly complicated and weird. Some of them advocated the outright use of black magic. Another involved a trained dog! The enterprising master of the animal took him to Greenwich and painstakingly trained him to bark loudly at noontime each day. The idea was that on a ship, wherever it was, the dog would bark at the same moment, thus notifying the navigator that it was noon back in Greenwich. On a tossing ship however, it was found that the poor creature lost all track of time, so another scheme went overboard.

The Royal Navy turned down nobody, however, no matter how wild and improbable his plan seemed to be. The stakes were enormous, so each inventor was given a fair trial. The Navy ran many such test voyages. The hopeful "scientist" was simply kept below decks while the ship made a run of a few weeks to sea. All he had to do was to come topside at the chosen moment and calculate the longitude. Nobody could do it.

By 1714 all methods had either failed, or, in the case of lunar sights, were too complex and unreliable. The thinking of scientists and astronomers had shifted back to efforts to construct a reliable clock. The British Board of Longitude offered the princely reward of 20,000 pounds to any clocksmith who could turn the trick. Metals, gearcutting, and machining had progressed far enough by now that there was hope, and the reward was claimed by many people. The Board of Longitude patiently examined all candidates and finally, in 1775, did bestow the reward in part to a London clocksmith. The mechanism which he had designed and built passed its tests. It could keep time close enough to be of practical value. The reason they only gave him part of the reward was that his clock, or chronometer, was very large and unwieldy, took endless time to build, and was extremely expensive.

Over the years improvements were made to increase accuracy, to reduce its cost, and to reduce its size and weight. Considerable progress was made to eliminate these objections, but the chronometer was still not widely accepted. It was still too costly, still not accurate enough, still regarded with great suspicion. Traditional methods were wasteful of time on voyages, and ships were lost, but mariners for the most part clung to the old ways. Now and then an occasional prosperous captain with an inquiring mind and a flair for mathematics would buy such a timepiece and hope he could figure a way that would enable him to determine his longitude.

So it was that for a variety of reasons, chronometers at first were not much used. Scientists and astronomers turned their attention once again to efforts to solve the problem of determining Greenwich time by lunar sights. Difficult and unreliable though they were, it was hoped that if better methods could be devised for taking the sights, they would be more satisfactory than dependence on a chronometer.

As the *Henry* cleared Salem and as Captain Prince sat in the ship's saloon pondering his course and the general question of longitude, he had hopes that his seasick second mate and clerk, Nathaniel Bowditch, could provide answers.

There are two good things about seasickness: it is not a fatal malady, and it doesn't last very long. Nat didn't die in spite of his misery, although at times he thought he was going to and probably wished he would. He had his usual bouncy health back in a few days.

[93]

As the ship made her course southward, soon were gone the wintry skies and the awesome, foam-topped seas that raced down out of the north like steely mountains over which the little *Henry* had to climb and labor. The insane scream of wind in the rigging softened too, and there came the day when the warm breeze of the southern ocean wandered through the lines and stays with a gentle murmur of welcome to the ship and her company. And also, like a daily miracle, the arch of the heavens above and the swelling sea below turned blue, deepening and melting finally to an incredible sapphire.

There finally came the day when the winds were gone and the *Henry* twisted and wallowed listlessly on the metallic seas of the equatorial calms. She pitched and staggered on the breathless water. Neptune himself seemed fast asleep; his occasional writhing and turning that moved the ship seemed but the vague movements of a being moving in his slumber, disturbed in his dreams. The ship's company baked beneath the glistening sun. The tar in her deck seams bubbled and oozed, while the panting crew ran from halyards to braces, eternally swinging the yards this way and that, trying to catch the tiniest wisp of breeze. Prince kept the weary men at it day and night, patiently working across the calm.

The clean, white, extra-heavy canvas which the *Henry* had flown when she left Salem was unshipped and stowed below. In its place were sent aloft the light-weather sails —the old rags which could not be trusted in a gale. They were discolored and crisscrossed with repairs and patches. The ship looked like a disreputable old bird, white wings stained and darkened with grime and dust.

At long last the ship passed out of the doldrums. One

fine morning, just as though a visible line had been crossed, the vessel passed from calm to wind. She heeled gently as the sails caught the power. The breeze quickly freshened and soon a necklace of diamonds sparkled beneath her bow. She raced on, day and night, in the driving thrust of the South Atlantic trades, those ancient and beloved winds of sailing-ship mariners.

On and on she went, day after day, week after week, a little speck under the immensity of sky above. The men worked quietly about the ship by day. At night they drew together in companionship in the cool downdraft from the swelling sails. Bathed in the light of a moon so bright it seemed a gleaming image of the sun itself, the men danced the hornpipe, played the concertina, and yarned endlessly, telling sailors' stories of the sea and its mysteries.

On the ship drove, and then, once more, she was in the grip of calms. She had reached the horse latitudes, far, far to the south now from her native New England. The *Henry* rolled and wallowed fearsomely. The sails and spars slatted and banged, and once more, day and night, the crew was kept hard at it, bracing the yards to wring movement from the most wandering gasp of wind.

There was a difference, though, from the equatorial doldrums. The sun was not so hot. The air held a touch of coolness. The seas were huge and glassy, and they came from every direction, seeming at times to rise straight up from the depths of the South Atlantic itself. Never had Nat dreamed a barometer could read so high. The very clouds rose towering to awesome heights, obeying some unseen natural force like that which affected the barometer, urging them higher and higher.

As they worked their way across the belt of the horse

latitudes, Prince daily became more cautious, more alert. He sniffed the air, scanned the sky and clouds, spent long hours watching the surface of the water. Finally one day he ordered the light canvas to be taken down. In its place were sent up the board-stiff heavy sails. To Nat's questioning, he merely responded briefly with "We must be prepared for a change in weather," and got on with his business of making his ship ready.

Then one day it happened. Quite suddenly the vessel heeled and began to pick up way. The helm was put over on a new course and almost before Nat realized what had happened they were flying again, this time south by east. They had made the roaring forties, and the farther south they worked the stronger the wind became, the higher the seas, the colder the weather.

Even to Nat's landsman's eyes and senses, there was no mistaking the authority and the weight of this wind. One look at the chart told why. The ship was nearing the end of the land. She was approaching the tips of the continents of South America and of Africa, even though in mid-Atlantic. The winds were now racing freely across almost half the world, over the unbroken ocean, with little or no land masses to disturb their flow and diminish their power.

These were the great westerlies of the southern oceans, the greatest current of wind on the globe.

Sailing ships bound to a western destination and going around Cape Horn had to face these winds, beat into them and old shellbacks prayed to all the gods of the ocean for a safe passage. Cape Stiff, as these old-timers called the Horn, was not for the fainthearted. Here the winds and the seas were without any land at all to temper their strength. Compressed into a funnel between South America and the masses of ice and land in Antarctica, their power and fury reached fearsome dimensions.

For ships such as the *Henry,* who were bound *away* from Cape Horn eastward toward the Cape of Good Hope at the tip of Africa, the problem was different. Instead of bucking into the seas and wind, she was running with them, running with all sails full and drawing, running fast and dangerously, with the ship ever fighting for her head, wanting to pay off from the wind, to run sideways and broach in the troughs of the seas.

The *Henry* plunged and bucked and the wind howled through the rigging from astern. The work was wet and hard for all hands and it took two men on the big wheel now to keep the ship at her business. Captain Prince issued strict orders to the helmsmen never to look astern, for the sight of a great curling monster racing up behind was enough to cause a man to lose his nerve and run from his job. Each time a wave roared up from behind, the little *Henry* seemed about to be overwhelmed, to stumble, but she always recovered triumphantly and careened onward, crazily, like a drunken man, into the next long valley.

Prince drove her hard, for here good time could be made, but there was no rest for anyone. The amount of sail the ship carried was crucial: too little and she'd stagger helplessly, an easy victim to the seas piling up from behind; too much and she could be driven straight under the water as she labored up from the hollows. The men continually furled canvas, and let it fly again as the wind rose and fell from day to day.

When the *Henry* left Salem and made good her course to the South, like the weather, Nat's spirits had improved. When he got his sea legs, his heart lifted and left behind the gray hopelessness and the frustrations which had plagued him. He began to take an interest in the ship and what made her move and live. He began learning, for the first time in his life, something of the beauty and the lithe grace of a square-rigger on the wide ocean. He slowly began changing his mind too, about the men who sailed the ship. He saw the back-breaking work, the drudgery, the discipline which these queens of the sea demanded of those who sailed in them.

Nat learned the names of the lines and stays, the yards, the sails and the commands necessary for every evolution and change of course. They were fantastic in number and the sequence which every detail had to be made in order for a change to be accomplished had to be precisely timed, and exact, or the consequences would have been disastrous.

Most of all, Nat's admiration for Captain Henry Prince soared as he observed the consummate skill with which that fine mariner drove his ship, drove it hard, and yet protected her and the men from mishap. He saw how the captain squeezed the last ounce of lift and drive out of the wind that he safely could. The vast planes of canvas were slacked, tightened, trimmed, braced here and about by the weary men, much as a soaring bird adjusts its wings to the turbulent air. Far from calling him a "dull ox" because of his deficiences in mathematics, Nat's opinion of his captain and friend changed completely. He understood now why Elias Hasket Derby had entrusted his most valuable ships and cargoes to this captain. Prince had only been nineteen years old when he commanded his first Derby ship and since that time had sailed them over most of the world, following the sea routes blazed by other

Salem "boy-skippers" before him, and extending them even farther.

As Nat's knowledge of the ship grew, he began taking a more active part in its operation. He was supposed to stand a watch and his pride drove him very hard. In all honesty however, it soon became apparent that he was not going to make a very impressive bucko mate. He just wasn't cut out for it! He stood his watch, but during those times he was on duty, Prince slept very lightly and always made sure that the helmsman and members of the crew on watch were the more capable and most experienced of the entire company. Nat finally settled to become a sort of "assistant to the helmsman!"

If Nat wasn't going to impress anybody as a watch-officer, in another sense he began to evoke Prince's deepest admiration. It quickly became apparent as the ship made her passage, that Nat's angry talk and defense of arithmetic navigation, was not simply idle or pompous boasting.

Eight

If Nat Bowditch was surprised at the complexity of
Captain Prince's job and impressed by the skill and wis-
dom which he brought to it, Prince in his turn was
utterly amazed at Nat's ability. He soon had the awesome
feeling that here, on the tossing little *Henry,* history was
being made. At long last, after thousands of years of
fumbling by mariners of every nation, he, Captain Prince,
had somehow blundered his way into signing on a man who
could, apparently without any trouble, read the stars
accurately enough to determine a fix.

Prince was far too careful a captain to trust the navigation of his ship as yet to such an unproved quantity as
Nat's "arithemetic." The *Henry* was navigated by the
usual methods but as the voyage wore on, Prince more
and more had the feeling that he was losing time, that

he was only fumbling his way across the ocean. If he had had more courage, he might simply have turned the navigation over to his scrawny little clerk and sailed the ship on the courses laid out for him. But he did not, and in all truth, could not be blamed. What Nat was doing was too incredible to be believed at first sight.

What Prince did do was to give Nat absolute freedom to experiment and calculate as much as he wished. For Nat this was a priceless gift. He badly needed the chance to perfect his skills and his methods under actual conditions at sea. Considering the low esteem in which most mariners held celestial navigation, Prince's enthusiasm and assistance provided Nat a rare opportunity. The voyage to Bourbon was a test run for him; the wide Atlantic a proving ground.

He found that he was right in everything which he had believed and had defended so stanchly against the jeers and the incredulity of Salem's seafaring community. At every turn it was demonstrated to Prince just how much Nat must had endured in the face of this animosity.

Prince, for example, had thought that he was skilled in determining his latitude. Nat devised completely new methods that for accuracy and speed made his seem like an exercise for beginners.

He also owned a very expensive pocket watch and kept it with him always. In this respect, the *Henry* was unlike most ships which could not even boast of such a navigational refinement as this. The watch was in no sense a chronometer, but Prince had used it for years as a day-to-day running check on the local time. He was proud of it, but Nat's daily time sights proved the watch to be so erratic that it was dangerous to rely on it at all. Any watch or clock which has a constant rate of loss or gain is useful to a navigator. He has only to add or subtract this steady gain or loss to each day's calculations; but when a timepiece loses time one day and gains the next, or vice versa, it becomes useless. Daily Nat checked the watch against his celestial timekeepers, and soon Prince was willing to relegate his cherished timepiece to the bottom drawer of his locker and use it henceforward, as he said, "to impress the ladies when he was ashore."

In the matter of longitude, however, Nat simply amazed the captain. By using the traditional type of lunar sights he was able to give Prince a daily figure in longitude. These sights had to be shot at night, of course, because they depended upon the relative position of the moon and certain stars. They also had to be taken during periods of calm, or when the vessel was hove to. They were so delicate and so complex that accuracy was impossible if the ship was moving about a great deal.

The mathematics of these lunar sights also was incredibly complicated. As Prince sat in the saloon watching Nat do his figuring, and saw the papers and the calculations on the slate pile up, he wondered truly whether or not such excursions would ever be practical for unlettered seamen. Even Nat, impatient as he was to see celestial navigation in wide use at sea, had to agree with Prince that what he was doing might never be practical unless it could be simplified enormously.

In addition to the astronomy and celestial navigation, Nat commenced what was to be a steady habit as long as he made voyages. He began to keep in his journal a log of everything about the passage which could conceivably be of use to mariners. He amended the charts, observed and jotted down information about tides, winds, currents, cloud formations, and other related data. So imprecise were the records of the times that even in this effort he was pioneering. Such information of course had long been a part of the lore of the sea but it had never been collected and put down in a useful, co-ordinated fashion. To Nat's precise and orderly mind, such helter-skelter disorder was unbearable.

So the *Henry* slowly made her easting, driven by the whistling winds of the roaring forties. As the ship approached the coast of Africa, Prince became more and more concerned about his position. Nat daily gave him their position in longitude, but this was not enough; he still did not have enough trust in the mathematics. If Nat's calculations were off, disaster could easily strike and the vessel be driven ashore. Almost by instinct, Prince now began to use all the knowledge and information which years of experience had stored away in his mind. "Seaman's eye," "seaman's feel"—these were what counted; these were what a man could rely on. These were "real" things, not abstractions like numbers and calculations on a slate or piece of paper.

Thus Captain Prince, like the Ancient Mariner himself, took his ship cautiously up to the land, using information and tricks that had been tried and true for thousands of years.

A seaman was posted to heave the lead. Hourly his monotonous report drifted back to the officers on the poop deck, to Nat Bowditch below in the saloon, working on his figures. "No bottom, sir." "No bottom, sir," went the steady refrain. The flight of birds was watched closely.

Were they sea birds, or were they land birds? If the latter, did they appear tired, lost, or thirsty? Was there anything else about them, and the direction from which they had come, that might give a clue as to how far off the coast lay? The clouds that rose ahead of the ship in the evenings—towering columns of white and gray and pink—began to have a different look to them. Even Nat could sense the difference. They seemed to soar higher; their bases were flatter. There surely had to be land somewhere there, hot beneath the sun. Lookouts were set to keep track of seaweed or driftwood. Had it been long in the water? Was it fresh from the mouth of a river or beach? Had it been recently torn from coastal rock? Was it waterlogged or buoyant?

Each and every one of these things were fed into Prince's mind, evaluated, assessed. Slowly the inescapable conclusions began to form, to flow outward like magic from the captain to entire crew. It was a feeling, a sense of finality, a sense of irrevocable definition that emanated from the worried, responsible figure of Prince as he cautiously probed the sea and the sky and worked his ship closer to shore. Every man on the ship felt it.

Nat too knew the *Henry* was approaching the coast. His figures told him so, but in spite of his trust in their accuracy, he found himself looking to Prince for confirmation. He was utterly fascinated by the superb display of seamanship as the captain reached out with all his senses to utilize sea lore that came from farther back than anyone could remember, far back in the mists of antiquity, in the time when sailors first put to sea—and it agreed with his mathematics!

Prince paused briefly as he ate his evening meal. The

[104]

steward brought it to him on the poop now. He didn't go below and wouldn't until land had been sighted. He looked at Nat. "Sure you're right, Nat. We're very close. It won't be long now."

Next day the color of the water changed. The blue of the Atlantic had been fading, turning to blue-green and then, suddenly, there was no more blue left at all. The bottom had shoaled to the continental shelf. The currents became different. One could feel it, could feel the additional rudder necessary to keep the head of the ship on her course as the current tried to pull it off.

Still that monotonous report of the leadsman—"No bottom, sir," but it couldn't go on. They *had* to be closing the coast and suddenly there it was . . . the leadsman swung his long line with the big lead weight on the end in a great looping swing, just as he had done constantly, ahead of the ship. He drew it back to him as the *Henry* moved ahead. The sailor stiffened. He didn't need to say anything. With the line right vertical below him, he jigged it up and down. Quite obviously the lead was touching something.

The man's voice rang through the ship in a shout of quiet triumph. "Thirty fathoms, sir. Thirty fathoms."

Prince looked at Nat with a gleam in his eye but he said nothing. The water shoaled rapidly. The bottom was slanting upward. Prince nodded to the bos'n, and on the next sounding, the hollow in the bottom of the lead weight was smeared with tallow.

When the sailor brought it up this time, Prince went forward and examined it himself. He nodded, satisfied. He knew exactly where he was, how many miles off the coast he was. There was gray ocean mud on the tallow.

Slowly the *Henry* continued on her course, rocking like an enormous cradle in the gentle sea. The day ended and all through the night, samples of the bottom were brought up for Prince's inspection. Before Nat's fascinated eyes, Prince spelled out for him what the bottom of the ocean was like off the coast of Africa. The gray mud changed to yellow. The yellow gave way to small rocks and pebbles and they changed to bits of shells and sand. This was close enough.

Prince ordered the ship hove to. They would wait until daylight. Nat took careful moon sights and sights again at dawn. He put their position about ten miles offshore and perhaps twenty miles north of the Cape. Showing the figures to Prince he felt a little foolish and humble. The captain hadn't needed him to make a proper landfall.

Prince laughed at Nat's embarrassment. "Never mind, Nat," he said. "You keep at your mathematics. If I'd followed your courses all the way from Salem, we would have been here a lot sooner. And besides, this landfall was easy. They're not all like this, Nat."

Nat looked at him, questions in his eyes.

"That's right. This was easy. I've been here many times before and I know this coast like I know Salem channel. Suppose you're on a strange coast. In the dead of night. In a fog or in a gale that's been blowing a month? Different then, my lad. This sort of seamanship is great but yours is the navigation of the future."

Next morning the ship came to life with the hail from the masthead at dawn. "Land Ho. Land Ho."

There was Africa, a low, thickening of the horizon, a tenuous, dark stretching band dividing the sea and the sky and beginning to shimmer and dissolve and glow in the early rose of dawn.

Prince and Nat looked at each other. There was admiration and affection in their eyes and respect too, for what each had done.

The hands were called, full sails were set, and soon the *Henry* was flying down the coast toward Cape Town, with the land looming larger now, purple and solid on the port side. That afternoon they rounded the Cape of Good Hope itself, cutting in close to the land, rising and falling on great seas, which, like fantastic monsters of the deep, welled up out of the currents of all the South Atlantic as they swept around the southernmost tip of the continent.

The *Henry* kept steadily on her way, using the great bulk of Table Mountain as a departure point. The Cape must have looked as it had three hundred years before, when Vasco da Gama, a Portuguese mariner trained in the school of Prince Henry, rounded it. Da Gama was searching for a route to the fabled Indies and as his frail little ship beat its way around the land, he called it the Cape of Good Hope, with the fervent prayer that it just might be the "cape of the good hope of the Indies."

Prince laid a course north by east, and on the afternoon of May 7, 1796, the island of Bourbon lifted herself like a lovely princess up out of the ocean to welcome the tired men on the *Henry*. The pilot came aboard, and by ten that night, the ship was safely anchored at Port Saint Denis. Like a beautiful swan she folded her wings and rested, swinging quietly on her cable. She had been at sea for four months.

Before turning in, Nat Bowditch leaned quietly on the

rail and gazed landward. Saint Denis lay in an arc of the coast, at the foot of dark volcanic mountains. Its lights glimmered feebly but in welcome. Above the mountains, stars burned steadily, filled with an abundance of fire that seemed to spill like water from a brimming vessel and to tumble in silvery cascades down to the sea.

Nat had completed his first voyage. As with all men, his true element was not the sea, and his senses—hungry for the land—were deeply stirred. A gentle offshore breeze drifted from the island, bringing with it strange fragrances —spices, coffee, smoke from charcoal braziers, pervasive odors of rotting leaves and decay from swampy ground. These were not the scents of his native New England but they were the scents of earth, and of man, and they were rich and heady after the months of the austere cleanliness of the sea.

Prince stood beside Nat, but the two men did not speak. The whole ship was still and quiet, bewitched and dreaming in the night, resting easily and far removed from the hustle and clamor of the voyage just completed. Nat watched a thin silver sickle of moon soar up from behind the mountains in the sky and for once felt no urge to run for his sextant!

Prince went forward to examine the anchor cable. He noted how the ship lay; he took rough bearings on the land and then, giving brief instructions to the man who was left on anchor watch, he went below for the first good sleep he had had in many months. He had brought his ship and her people to harbor and could now rest briefly.

The next morning Captain Prince and his clerk were rowed ashore in the ship's boat. This was Nat's first foreign port, and it was a very beautiful one. Bourbon was a tropical island, with palms and mangroves along the coast, but its hillsides were clothed in the dark green of hardwood trees. Cool streams flowed in silvery cascades down the volcanic heights and ran through the town and its suburbs, making the parks delightful places to find relief from the hot sun. There were woods of bamboos and forests of mangoes, flowers everywhere, and mountainside fields green with coffee bushes.

Bourbon—it is now called Réunion—was a French colony. Its people were lonely and extremely hospitable. Nat and Prince spent much time ashore and were welcome guests in the homes of Saint Denis, and everywhere Nat was enchanted by the beauty and the warmth which was offered by the island and its people.

Unloading of the ship started almost immediately. There was no dock and all the cargo had to be taken ashore in lighters—a slow, difficult process when high seas were running. The tedious task was also complicated by the heavy rains which fell during this season of the year.

The *Henry* carried a general cargo, some of which was consigned to merchants in the town. The rest had to be sold openly. Nat's admiration for Prince as a seagoing businessman soon was as great as his admiration of him as a mariner. Nat's head for figures was more than useful as the two of them wove a tricky path through the maze of prices, quantities, money exchange, and so on. Finally everything was sold, delivered ashore, and paid for, in credits in the countinghouses of the merchants, or in gold. The gold piled up in the ship's strongbox and would be taken back to Salem. The credits were to be used to buy coffee—the return cargo.

Nat also had his own business affairs to take care of. His adventure went at a very good profit—more than 300 per cent, and he felt very pleased with himself. On Prince's advice, he used the money to purchase a return adventure—a quantity of spices which he hoped to sell at a profit again in Salem.

The coffee for the *Henry* came in very slowly, much too slowly for Prince. The ship had been four months in Saint Denis, and the holds were far from full. Prince decided to leave the port and to sail clear around the island, stopping at each small bay and jetty where coffee might be purchased. Eventually, in a driving rain, through a high surf on the beach, the last of it came aboard—more than a hundred tons it took to top off the hatches. Several days later, after five weary months spent unloading and loading, the *Henry* was battened down and cleared for home.

They coasted back down to the Cape of Good Hope, rounded it, and headed north and west. As the land vanished astern, as the deep glassy swells gave way to the more savage seas of the Atlantic, and as the ship heeled to the drive of the westerlies, Nat's heart exulted. It was good to be back at sea and to be going home.

He and Captain Prince sat in the saloon; it was already noisy and clamorous as the little *Henry* settled down to the long job. Nat was finishing up his work on the ship's cargo manifests; Prince was sipping a glass of ruby port. At top of the companionway showed a gray square of clouds; a yellow, wintry Atlantic sun glimmered.

"Nat?" Prince said.

Nat looked up.

"Nat, do you think you could lay out a course for me?"

Nat smiled. "Yes," he said. He knew what it meant.

The *Henry* was going to cross the ocean by celestial navigation.

The weather was as foul as any Prince had ever seen. Gale after gale whistled down upon the laboring ship, and when they let up briefly it was to leave her wallowing and panting in the horse latitudes and the doldrums. But on she went, happy, it seemed, to know she was going in a straight line, guided by numbers gleaned from the heavens.

One evening as Prince watched Nat deep in the maze of calculations, he said, "Nat, do you really think all ships will be steered by celestial navigation one day?" He was not joking.

Nat looked up; he said a bit sourly, "We're doing it, aren't we?"

Prince nodded.

Nat continued. "And you know that this voyage home is the fastest you ever made across this ocean. And you know the reason."

"Yes, I know," Prince said. "You've made the point about the shortest distance. I won't quarrel with you. But what I meant was"—he gestured to the pile of paper work—"I mean . . . *you* can do it. *I* can't. I can't even grasp the astronomy, let alone do the mathematics. I don't think very many others can either. Too complicated."

Nat started to bluster, but then he grinned a bit and said, "So. I suppose it is. Complicated."

For a moment the two men were quiet, then Prince said, "Why don't you make it simple, Nat?"

Make it simple. It was an idea that hadn't occurred to Nat. It all seemed simple to him.

"Face it, Nat," continued Prince. "If you want *sailors* to use celestial navigation, you'll have to simplify. Otherwise forget it."

Nat looked down at his papers and at the slate. They were covered with figures and formulas, all of which did seem simple to him. But still, perhaps Prince was right. He looked up. "What about it does appear too complicated, Henry? To you, for example."

Prince apparently had done some thinking about this. "Two things," he said promptly. "First is the way you take lunar sights. It's too difficult. Too many chances for error, and I must say I can scarcely grasp the concept behind it. Find a new way to take lunars."

"And then?"

"Then make the mathematics simpler. Plain arithmetic instead of calculus or spherical trigonometry and solid geometry and whatever else it is you use. That's for astronomers, not for sailors. Express it all in simple tables or formulas that we don't have to understand."

"But that's for mud-brains," said Nat.

"All right, call us mud-brains or anything else you please. That won't solve the problem."

In disgust Prince turned to stomp up the ladder to the poop.

Nat blushed. He was too fond of this old friend to talk like this. "I didn't mean it, Henry," he apologized.

Prince turned, halfway up the ladder. "Nat," he said, "you still don't see it. It's easy for you but impossible for the rest of us. You believe in celestial navigation, and I must say, I do too now. But if you want sailors to use it, then simplify. Like it or not, that's the way it'll have to be."

"But they already have made up tables and formulas," said Nat.

"They don't work," Prince said simply. "They don't work. And don't ask me why. Such matters are beyond my mud-brains. *You* figure it out."

At long last, three months after leaving Bourbon, Nat looked up from his calculations and said to Prince, "Tomorrow you should pick up the Massachusetts coast."

Said Prince, "I know."

"You know? How?"

Prince grinned. "Just the old sailor in me says so." He looked at the clouds, at the sea, felt the wind. "I've brought too many ships home to Salem not to know the signs."

Nat looked at Prince. There was a hurt expression on the little clerk's face. "You didn't trust me, did you?"

Prince howled with laughter. "Not that, Nat. I trust you. But I'm also a sailor and I trust what *that* tells me. See? Now we have two checks on our position."

Nat had to smile. He nodded in agreement, then Prince continued seriously. "I'm truly grateful, Nat. This is the fastest passage I ever made across the South Atlantic. And *you* did it. But one thing. Let's not talk about it ashore. Remember Mr. Derby. He might have a stroke or fire me."

After almost one year at sea, the *Henry* sailed up the channel into Salem Harbor.

Nat was sure to pack his journal in his seabag that night when he went ashore. Scribbled at the bottom of the pages dated December 26, 1795, Christmas Day, and filled in with several complex diagrams and computations, was the simple, brief entry: "Last Thursday thought of a new way of taking lunars."

Nine

In March 1796, some two months after Prince and Bowditch returned to Salem in the *Henry,* Elias Hasket Derby took formal possession of a brand-new ship.

In those days New England vessels bore names as solid and workaday as the merchants who owned them. They wandered on the most distant seas of the world, concluding their traffic in the most exotic ports, but their names were the austere, no-nonsense names of their home harbors, as for example, the *Annie Smith,* the *Archibald M. Dorset,* the *Oliver Higgins,* or, perhaps even more simply— *Jennie,* or *Mary* or *Sally.* No such prosaic name awaited Derby's new ship.

Derby must have had a romantic streak buried beneath his crusty exterior. He also knew his Greek mythology and searched the old legends for exactly the right name.

In classical Greek religion, Astraeus was the son of Titans. His wife was Eos, goddess of the Dawn. His children by her were the winds and the stars. Derby christened his new ship the *Astrea*, hoping perhaps as it ranged the world, it would sail with confidence, with authority over all the winds and the stars.

At this time, around the end of the 1700s, Boston and Salem were locked in a deadly struggle to become the queen city of American shipping. The Far East—Asia, the Indies—was the prize. Richer than any man could dream, it was opening to trade with the West and was like a dangling, golden plum to be harvested by those with courage and daring. So the ships constantly probed deeper and deeper into the heart of the Orient.

Derby had a bold plan. Boston ships sailed south to Cape Horn, thrashed their bitter passage into the Pacific, and then laid a course north and west. Salem ships took the other route. They crossed the Atlantic, doubled the Cape of Good Hope then headed north and east across the Indian Ocean. Derby decided he would send a ship where no Salem vessel had ever gone—clear to Manila, the treasure house of the East, the trading post of the Orient. The merchant who had secure connections in the Philippines, and a reliable route there, was but a short step from the fabulous ports of China.

To blaze such a route, Derby needed a special kind of a ship and for this purpose the *Astrea* had been built. She was big and heavy for the long, dangerous voyage. She was deep and beamy but with clean lines for speed. For driving power she carried an enormous spread of canvas: when set, her wings seemed like towering masses of white clouds.

Beside the *Astrea*, the little *Henry* seemed an ugly barn-yard duckling.

Derby spent a fortune outfitting the ship. Her canvas and rigging were the heaviest and strongest to be bought. Her masts were lofty, her spars massive. She was also heavily armed, for vessels venturing into such waters in those times frequently had to defend themselves. The *Astrea* had a full arsenal of the usual small weapons and, in addition, mounted a formidable battery of nineteen cannon.

Derby selected a special crew for this ship. For captain he chose his most competent man, Henry Prince. For super-cargo and second mate, Nathaniel Bowditch was signed. Nat wasn't much of a ship's officer but he had more than earned his way on the voyage of the *Henry*.

Prince was extremely pleased to have Nat with him again. He could forgive Nat's fumbling attempts to stand a watch in exchange for the tremendous job he could do in taking care of the cargo, arranging for payments and threading his way through the pitfalls of foreign banking and money exchange.

Captain Prince also had another reason to be pleased. He had been congratulated from one end of Salem to the other for the fast voyage of the *Henry*, and no matter what Derby or anyone else thought, he knew the *real* reason. It wasn't his seamanship, excellent though it had been, but rather it was Nat Bowditch's navigation. He wanted a repeat if possible, with the new ship.

At last all was ready, and the *Astrea* moved down to Salem from the shipyard in Bradford where she had been built. Her hull rose higher than Derby wharf itself, and her masts towered far above the huge warehouse. Loading commenced at once.

Derby and Prince had decided on a mixed cargo which seemed to include a bit of just about everything that humming New England shops, forges, and factories could produce. For days the cargo poured into the *Astrea*'s yawning holds—hats, clothes, nails, shoes, chains, plows, copper, lead, pots, pans, glassware, lamps, and much, much more. Nat was busy from morning to night. Everything had to be carefully tallied, costs noted, where it was stowed diagramed out. Space also had to be left for casks of wine which Prince planned to load in Madeira on the outward leg. It was hoped the wine would bring a good price from thirsty Manilans.

As Nat so efficiently took over the job of looking after the cargo, Captain Prince was most pleased to relax in the company of seafaring cronies and was quite the envy of them all. It was no small thing to be relieved of the detail paper and number work which the supercargo took over so easily.

When Nat had packed his seabag on the *Henry* and walked down the gangplank, he found quite magically that Salem seemed to have changed somewhat in its attitude toward him.

He still wasn't exactly popular. Too many people had smarted under the lash of his acid tongue in the past, and they still remembered. Others were jealous of his new status—he was an officer on a blue-water ship and he'd gotten there the easy way, they thought. Most Salem boys had to fight and claw their way up "through the hawse-pipe." They could only hope for a berth as an officer after a long apprenticeship before the mast. Nat Bowditch had made it to his berth off the main saloon "through the cabin window," because he knew about numbers!

Nevertheless, he had made a long voyage on a fast and profitable ship. Elias Derby and Prince spread the word about town as to how valuable he was as a ship's clerk, and there was no doubting such authorities as these. Whether anybody liked it or not, Nathaniel Bowditch was now a member of the Salem seagoing fraternity and an accepted member of the most prominent ship-owning firm in town.

He took Prince's advice not to say a word about the navigation, and his own common sense kept him from boasting about his quite modest exploits as a seaman. In another area, though, being very human, he talked and was listened to with respect. His knowledge was accurate and to the point when it came to consular fees, stevedoring fees, currency exchange, and everything else connected with trading in a foreign port. There was no doubt about it: he knew the subject and eventually it was conceded that if more young fellows like Nat Bowditch were aboard Salem's ships they would make even more profits.

Little wonder Nat swaggered a bit for the first time in his life. He was diminutive, and thin, but he was sunburned and had the look of a deep-water man in his eyes. In Salem these commanded respect.

His step was a little jauntier for another reason, too. The adventure had turned out very well. The box of spices returned him a handsome profit, and this money, plus the wages he had earned on the voyage, made him a man of means. For somebody who'd never had *any* money, this slight prosperity was a most enjoyable state of affairs. It meant he could now sport a new suit of clothes, a decent hat, and proper shoes. These things, important though they were, dwindled beside something else. He could now embark on a little courting!

Elizabeth Boardman was as sprightly a Salem lass as ever threw an inviting glance at a promising young sailor. She was the daughter of a shipmaster who had been lost at sea, and she lived with her mother in a fine big white house on Salem Common. Nat settled down to woo Elizabeth with a campaign as devastating and thorough as any he would ever devise for plotting the path of a meteor. Elizabeth and her mother were impressed.

Each night he was welcomed to the big house and here, in the elegant parlor, amidst the mementoes of the late captain's voyages, he courted Elizabeth. He wasn't exactly a maiden's dream of a handsome bucko mate, or a young captain with a command of his own, but there was something about Nat Bowditch that wrung Elizabeth's heart. She fell helplessly, head-over-heels in love, and her mother approved. There was an air of honesty and character in the little suitor that inspired the old lady's confidence. Under the warmth and affection showered on him by his sweetheart and her mother, Nat bloomed. Life seemed suddenly glorious, with a future in which anything was possible.

Naturally, when a young man is in love, he confides in his beloved his deepest hopes and dreams. Nat's dreams were romantic ones of mathematics and his hopes were that they could be used by Salem men when they took square-riggers to sea. In Mrs. Boardman and Elizabeth, he found an enthusiastic audience. They had lived their lives with a seafaring man; they could understand what Nat was talking about.

He solemnly discussed questions of latitude and longitude, the movement of the heavenly bodies. They ate it up and prodded him for more and finally in a burst of confidence, he blurted out what had happened on the *Henry*.

"Oh Nat," said Elizabeth, "then she was *truly* navigated."

Nat modestly allowed that this was so.

"Then you must tell everyone," said Elizabeth, her eyes glowing. "Think what it will mean."

A cold chill went through Nat. "No," he said. "We must keep quiet about that. Later, perhaps, but not now."

He then explained in detail what had happened and how most people felt about celestial navigation. It took many evenings and much explanation before he was able to get Elizabeth's promise to keep silent.

"I will not talk about the *Henry*," she said with determination, "but I will mention in a general way what you are doing."

Nat allowed no harm could come from this and privately hoped Derby wouldn't discharge him.

Mrs. Boardman asked, "The late captain used to say that celestial navigation had caused the loss of many a ship. And that the methods were far too complicated. Is this so?"

"Unfortunately, yes, Mrs. Boardman," said Nat.

"Then how is it, Mr. Bowditch, that you have been able to do what no one else could do?"

"It's because Nat is smarter than the others," snapped Elizabeth.

Nat mumbled, colored, then answered honestly. "The methods are very complicated," he said.

"Then it won't work with most seafaring men I know," said Elizabeth. "Nat, you'll have to simplify them. That's all."

The old lady was not so easily put off. "The captain also used to say the problem was one of longitude and time sights. He said that lunars could not be trusted."

Nat hesitated a long time. Then he said modestly, "I believe I have discovered a new and simpler way of taking lunars."

Mrs. Boardman and her daughter knew what this could mean. They'd heard it time and time again. Their eyes glowed.

"Oh, Nat," said Elizabeth. "I'm so very proud of you. Imagine!"

Nat's flat little chest swelled as though it would burst. Nobody had ever been proud of him before! Throughout all the years only his own faith and fierce love for the beauty of mathematics had kept alive his hopes and dreams. To have at last someone taking pride in him and understanding what he believed was an unbearable joy.

Nat and Elizabeth beamed at each other ecstatically. Mrs. Boardman beamed at each of them. The widow of a respected mariner, she knew the value of what Nat had done. Her own heart swelled with pride. Not every woman could look forward to a son-in-law who had invented a new method of taking lunar sights!

When the *Astrea* sailed a few days later, in the spring of 1796, Elizabeth and Nat had an "arrangement." They would be married when he returned. This was more than a year away, but Elizabeth settled down to wait, as the sweethearts of all sailors waited for their men to come home.

Nat had to finish one further problem before the ship left. He thought about it a long time and consulted a good many people. What should he take as an adventure this time?

He finally made up his mind and purchased a large number of small but very accurate marine compasses! Each compass was fitted in a strong and well-made wooden case, and he reasoned he might find a ready market for them among the owners of small boats, junks and schooners which plied the waters of the China Sea and among the Philippine Islands. Months later his only re-gret was that he hadn't brought along twice the number.

May 27 was a gala day in Salem. The *Astrea* was one of the largest ships ever to leave the port and she was bound on a trail-blazing voyage. She carried a tremendously valuable cargo, representing the hopes of not just Derby, but those of many other people in town. As she swung away from the dock and her white sails loosed to the wind, the cheers and fervent prayers of all the onlookers wished her good luck and safe passage. It was an important day in Salem.

Captain Prince got his ship under way with very little fanfare. He and his first mate handled the departure. Second Mate Bowditch prudently kept out of the way! The bellowing of orders to stomping seamen was not among his talents.

Prince was also concerned in another way about his ship. Every vessel is different in the way she handles, the way she responds to the planes of her sails, the way she answers her helm. A trial run or two about the bay was the

only opportunity Prince had had to feel out the *Astrea*.
She had handled beautifully; been sweet and nimble and
obedient, but Prince was understandably nervous. Big
sailing ships can be willful ladies. Sometimes they take on a
life and personality all their own that is completely unsus-
pected. They seem to do things for no other purpose than to
remind the men who man them that they'd better mind
their manners. Some are docile and quiet, some are fast,
others slow. Some are wild horses who can never be tamed,
who can never submit to the bit and saddle. These often
turn "killer" and take a steady and fearful toll of lives.

When the *Astrea* got under way on her maiden voyage,
she started off just as sweetly and nicely as could be wished.
She left the dock smoothly, swung around and allowed
herself to be pointed down the channel. An onshore
breeze was blowing, and it was necessary to work her in
short tacks, back and forth across the wide channel. She be-
haved beautifully for a few minutes, to the great relief
of Prince and all the shipwise audience ashore.

Suddenly, like the regal lady she was, the *Astrea* decided
to have a little fling and show these human beings who
really was boss. Coming about near the Marblehead
shore, Prince gave the necessary orders. The helm was put
up, the sails on the foremast were backed to swing her
head about on the new tack.

The *Astrea* simply refused to have anything to do with
such nonsense. She groaned, shuddered, shivered, and kept
on going straight ahead. A few minutes later, nicely and
prettily, she slid aground hard and fast on the mudbanks.
The crowd watching gasped in dismay. Derby threatened
to have his long-awaited apoplectic stroke and to fall
from the pier into the water.

Nat wanted to sink right through the deck and heaved a sigh of relief that he had had nothing to do with this particular bit of navigation. Prince nearly burst his throat bellowing orders and trying one trick after another to free the ship. To his eternal embarrassment, the *Astrea* refused to budge. Like a smug old dowager of the sea, in full view of the entire town, she snuggled down in the mud until, as the tide went out, she sat high and dry. She stayed that way throughout the night.

The following day, when the full tide came in, she deigned to let her fuming, sweating crew warp her off with a big kedge anchor which they hauled out to deep water in a small boat.

All hands gasped their thanks as she finally floated and bobbed quietly in mid-channel. They set sail again and headed seaward without a bit of trouble. She'd had her fun, taken a brief rest on a mud bank, and now was ready to settle down to the serious business of tackling the open ocean. Not a mast or shroud had been strained; not a seam had been opened. The only damage was to the pride of her crew.

On the broad sea the *Astrea* made up for her trouble. With a stiff half-gale whistling down on her port quarter and with her canvas swelling stiff and taut, she frolicked eastward across the Atlantic in just under thirty days.

There was no nonsense about who was doing the navigating. Prince wanted a fast passage, and there was only one way to get it. Drive the ship hard, straight across. He pushed hard day and night, right up to the coast of Europe, with complete faith in Nat's ability to tell him where they were.

Late one afternoon, just as Nat's arithemetic had predicted, the cry of "Land O" rang from the masthead. The longitude and latitude were perfect. There was Lisbon Rock, right on the nose, rising up in the distance out of the mists.

Nat's job was done; it was up to Prince now. All that night they stood off the coast, tacking slowly back and forth. Early in the morning the pilot flag soared to the main truck and a few hours later the *Astrea* swayed slowly up to her anchorage in the broad Tagus River.

Nat gazed over the water toward Lisbon. Here, he was in ancient and good company, traveling in the footsteps of the men who had done so much to make navigation possible. It was here, more than three hundred years before, that the curious and intelligent Portuguese Prince Henry had established his school for navigators. To it he had attracted the finest scholars of the times—mathematicians, astronomers, chartmakers, philosophers, and geographers —and together they had worked out and brought into one great system all that was known of celestial navigation and of the earth's geography. It was precisely the trail of the school's greatest sailor—Vasco da Gama—that the *Astrea* would now follow.

After a miserable hot trip, much of it nearly becalmed, when the ship was lucky to make fifteen or twenty miles a day, the *Astrea* dropped her anchor in Madeira, in the Azores. Soon the huge puncheons of wine were brought out to the open roadstead and loaded aboard. The last thing Prince did was to go ashore and buy a dozen small casks of the delicious port wine which was produced here. Half of it was for Derby and the other half for himself, to be stowed eventually in the cellar of the fine house he already had his eye on for retirement.

The ship headed south. No creeping along the coast for Bowditch, frightened to leave the sight of land. He laid a course several hundred miles to sea, to be well clear of the coast of Africa, and to pick up the clean ocean trades, and headed boldly for the Cape of Good Hope.

A month and a half later the Cape was rounded. The ship worked up to Bourbon for water and wood, then Prince piled on the canvas and, with a favorable monsoon, headed north and east into the Indian Ocean for Sumatra, which would be the next landfall.

Ten

The monsoon winds sweep down out of Asia, over the Indian Ocean, and across the seas and islands of the East Indies. For six months they blow unfailingly and strongly, always from the same direction. Then, they reverse themselves and blow steadily out of the oceans back up over the land again.

In and out, inhale and exhale, back and forth, back and forth, from the land to the oceans and from the oceans to the land. The monsoons are like the respiration of a giant, each gigantic breath taking six months to accomplish. They are a part of the life of our globe just as the unerring flight of the stars through the skies is a part of the greater movement of the universe.

The ancients believed that this massive back and forth sighing of the wind was arranged by the gods to bring rains for the harvests. Ancient mariners believed that they had been ordained by the gods of the sea to blow devout sailors safely to their destinations. With almost nothing else to guide them, these early voyagers could always rely on these providential winds, strong and unfailing in their direction, to drive their frail ships to port.

Today, of course, men know that there are other reasons for the regularity and the strength of the monsoons.

As the sun swings with the seasons, great masses of air over Siberia are heated and dried. They expand; high-pressure areas are created, and the air is forced to flow south, out over the oceans. By now the sun will have changed its path, and a low-pressure area has formed over the land. The moisture-laden air then flows in from the sea, dropping rain as it comes. Finally it swirls up and over the great mountain ranges, such as the Himalayas, where it is once again reheated, thoroughly dried, and then forced south to the sea. Thus the cycle is repeated endlessly, twice a year.

Mariners who had to rely on the wind to drive their ships, regulated their voyages by the monsoons, waiting until it was blowing in the direction they wanted to go. Without waiting for the favorable wind, they would have to tack continually, beating back and forth, literally clawing their way forward in the face of the adverse wind. Ships could do this, of course, but it was dangerous. Charts were unreliable, and captains did not know how to navigate properly, so a passage against the monsoon through unknown island waters was an extremely perilous undertaking. The lesser danger was simply to settle down in port and wait for the wind shift, even though this did lengthen passage time enormously.

Hence it was that when Prince left Salem in March, his hope was to get around Africa, into the Indian Ocean, and through the dangerous complex of reefs, islands, and shoals of the East Indies with the wind always behind him. This favorable summer, or wet, monsoon would be blowing in the general direction of the Philippines. Once in Manila, he planned to hurry his trading so that by the time he was ready to leave for home, the wind would have shifted and would now drive him safely to the south and west. Such planning was standard procedure for sailing ships. Prince was doing what any competent mariner would do.

So it worked out. The summer monsoon begins in May. Shortly after this, the *Astrea* had rounded Africa and watered at Bourbon Island. Then, swaying easily in the long deep blue swells of the Indian Ocean beneath her keel, she headed steadily north and east toward the Indies.

There was little problem in navigation except that Nat continually had to check longitude as they worked east. Prince knew exactly where he wanted to go, and the never-changing monsoon blew the ship steady and true as an arrow in flight. Bowditch never found Prince's calculations in error.

At last the cry of "Land O!" echoed from the main truck. Low and dark on the horizon lay the island of Sumatra. This was familiar ground to Prince. He closed the land, sighted mountains and capes which he knew, and then coasted until the waters opened into Sunda Strait and Java Head was broad on his starboard beam. Sunda Strait was the entryway for ships bound into the Indies from the West; the forbidding bulk of Java Head was the landmark.

[130]

Once among the Indies, there again was little problem for the navigator. Prince had been here many times and he knew the waters well. There were big islands, reefs, and rocky shores—all of them dangerous—with the bleached bones of many a ship on them to give sad evidence of this danger. Prince skirted them all confidently. With the wind behind the *Astrea,* the big ship was fast and maneuverable and since the wind direction was always from the same point of the compass, Prince could relate each piece of land to it and determine his position. Except for Nat's calculations, Prince never knew his *exact* position in longitude and latitude, but with the true monsoon blowing always, he could work his way safely through the dangers.

Nat found important work to do, though. He continually amended the charts in terms of precise mathematical positions. Daily he took the fixes and noted carefully each reef and island. These positions either were nonexistent on the charts or else the charts were so badly in error that they could not be trusted at all. He also worked steadily at perfecting his new method of taking lunar sights. Finally even he, whose passion was accuracy, was content. He was sure the method was reliable and that it was simple enough for any unlettered mariner, no matter how "tarry his thumbs," to master.

The days passed into weeks, the weeks into months, and at last the maze of the islands was left behind. The long run up the China Sea was done, and Luzon lay low and dark green on the horizon. Soon the ship had been worked down to Manila, the anchor let go and the voyage was complete. They had made good time: about six months. There was another American ship in the harbor but she was from Boston and had come across the Pacific. The *Astrea* thus was not the first vessel to fly the Stars and Stripes in Manila Bay, but she was the first Salem ship to do so.

The long days and nights at sea, when Nat had nothing more to do than revel in the joys of astronomy, sharpen up his lunar sights method, amend charts, and work out problems in calculus and trigonometry, were over! Other practical and immediate tasks were at hand.

The *Astrea* was run up the Pasig River and anchored so as to be more conveniently located for loading and unloading cargo. Nat and Prince rented a house ashore and commenced their negotiations.

They were long and tedious. There was but one word to guide them: *Beware.* The Spanish authorities were suspicious and out to feather their own nests whenever possible. The merchants to whom they sold were principally Chinese; these wily and astute traders missed no opportunity to drive ruinous bargains, either by honest or crooked methods. Manila was the great trading post of the Orient, and hundreds of huge Chinese junks brought cargo to it and returned to the mainland deeply laden with merchandise from the Western world. Nat noted in his journal that some of the cargoes brought by these great junks were valued at more than a million dollars! Captain Prince and Nat were not backward themselves, however, in driving hard bargains, and were able to dispose of their own cargo at excellent profits. Finally the last pot and pan and pair of shoes had been sold and delivered ashore and paid for. The ship commenced loading its return cargo.

They had decided to fill up with hides, with sugar, and with indigo. Nat was busy from morning till night supervising the incoming cargo and spent half his time, so it seemed to him, just keeping a wary and sharp eye out for chicanery. Over and over Prince was to thank his stars that Nat was with him. No moldy hides got past his suspicious inspection. He spotted damp sugar which could have given them no end of trouble on their homeward-bound voyage. He was able to buy indigo for seventy-five dollars per hundred pounds but when the bright blue stuff began to come aboard he found that much of it had been slightly dampened to make it weigh more. He solved this problem by accepting it only in three- or four-pound lots and dumping it out on the floor of the house where he and Prince lived. He became expert at detecting this shady practice, but imagine the labor it took to go through half a ship's cargo of indigo in three- or four-pound lots.

The language also was a terrible problem. There was no common tongue between the Americans and the Chinese, so Nat applied himself to learn enough spoken and written Chinese to conduct their business. This didn't fluster him in the least. To him it was no mystery; calm logic helped him thread his way through the complicated picture writing just as surely as it had helped him thread a way through the paths of the stars. As far as Chinese numbers went, numbers were numbers to Nat, wherever they began on a page and whatever they looked like! With his orderly, logical mind, he quickly mastered the Chinese system of counting and even wrote a piece about it to help other mariners.

Once again he was lucky with his adventure, and had no difficulty selling his compasses. Nat had paid two dollars apiece for them, and he found that the masters of junks, small gunboats, schooners, and other small island craft snapped them up for eight dollars each, a very handsome profit. He invested everything he had in the precious indigo for his homeward-bound adventure.

During all the dickering and trading and squabbling with rascally merchants and native traders, Prince kept a very sharp eye on the wind and weather and sky. The monsoon had shifted and was now blowing steadily in the opposite direction from that which had brought them to Manila. He knew he had only about six months of this wind and did everything possible to hurry the departure. The *Astrea* had to leave while there was still enough of the favorable monsoon left to allow sufficient time for her to get through the East Indies before the next shift.

By pushing very hard, Nat and Prince were finally able to conclude their business. A day or two before they were to sail, a near catastrophe struck them. They were robbed, while sleeping ashore their last night in the rented house, of a bag containing one thousand dollars in gold. Thieves placed two long bamboo poles against the outside of the building, climbed up them, and made off with the money. When they left they forgot to close a window, and the draft awakened Nat and Prince. The alarm was raised and some time later a police patrol boat found the robbers on the river in a canoe, dividing the spoils. In the excitement the canoe overturned and the gold fell to the bottom of the river. Many precious days were lost trying to fish it up but finally all but about one hundred dollars was recovered.

After this episode Captain Prince and his crew were more than happy to weigh anchor and head for home. They cleared Manila for Salem on December 12, 1796 and after an uneventful passage arrived home in May 1797.

The ship had been gone about fourteen months. By carefully planning to take advantage of the monsoon, Prince had turned in a phenomenally fast voyage. It was a milestone in another way as well, returning more profit for all concerned, in relation to the money invested, than any ship had ever done before sailing out of Salem. Import duties were extremely low in those days, but the duty alone paid on the *Astrea*'s cargo amounted to nearly twenty-five thousand dollars. The profits of the interested parties— Derby, Prince, to a lesser extent Bowditch and others of the town—ran to about 800 per cent!

Nat came ashore much richer in money. He was also now a very respected member of the seagoing fraternity and of the Derby establishment. The respect he really wanted, though, which should have come from his skill as a navigator, was denied him. If Derby noticed that not only was the cargo more properly managed on a ship which carried Nat Bowditch, but that the voyages were invariably faster, he kept his thoughts to himself.

Captain Prince by now was so impressed by Nat's skill that he spread the word that his supercargo was something very special when it came to laying a course in a straight line. He also passed it around that Nat had developed a new way to take lunar sights for longitude and that furthermore the method really worked.

A new way to take accurate lunars should have been enough to make any owner or master prick up his ears but the old traditions and bugaboos die hard. Nat received no acclaim. Shipmasters were in no sense ready to trust their ships and their navigation to such "incompetents" as the irascible little ex-clerk. After a few jeers and rebuffs, Nat held his peace. He was tired of arguing with stupidity, weary of being called a fool for standing up for something which he knew to be pure truth, and settled back into loneliness and silence.

The only bright spot in his life was the continuing courtship of Elizabeth Boardman. He was more than welcome at her home and spent many happy hours there. But marriage was out of the question. He simply didn't have enough money. As he couldn't spend *all* of his time at the Boardmans, he passed many lonely days and nights in his own room, endlessly calculating. With pencil and slate and paper, he spent his time doing problems in higher mathematics and computing orbits of the planets.

Word of what he could do with a sextant, however, and some mathematics, had reached a pair of ears that really listened. What happened was to have a profound influence on Nat Bowditch's life.

This first voyage on the *Astrea* proved two very important things. Nat had demonstrated over and over again, to his complete satisfaction, that his method of fixing longitude was absolutely reliable. He had also developed a new way to determine latitude which was so far superior to the old that it could be said he had invented an entirely new procedure.

However, this was only half the battle. The mathematics of celestial navigation were so complicated that they were far beyond the rough and ready abilities of the men who went to sea. And, to make matters worse, they took so long to do that their value was very small except in the hands of a real expert like Bowditch. If a fix were to be of real service, then the computations would have to be concluded in a reasonably short length of time.

Even Nat, short-tempered as he was with those who were less than mathematical wizards, recognized the need for simplification. How could such involved concepts and procedures be made easy? Over the centuries, attempts had been made to deal with this problem, and the most recent in Bowditch's time had been those of an Englishman named John Hamilton Moore.

These attempts took the form of books of tables, containing thousands of sets of figures for every possible altitude reading of the various stars used by navigators. The person using the tables didn't have to worry about astronomy, or know any calculus. This work had all been done for him and was included in each set of figures in the tables. Theoretically all a captain had to do was to apply his own celestial readings to the appropriate set of figures in the tables, and by means of simple formulas, plus addition and subtraction, find out where he was. As long as he could read a sextant properly, and remember his sums, presumably anybody could navigate.

The system didn't work. Moore's tables had been printed in England and were heralded as being at long last the answer to the problem. Many an open-minded captain, desiring faster voyages, had put his trust in arithmetic and Moore's tables and come to grief. In fact, much of the mistrust which mariners had for celestial navigation came from the worthlessness of the best book available on the subject, Moore's *The Practical Navigator*.

One evening, as Nat was dawdling away his time doing mathematical problems, there was a knock on his door. He admitted a young man who was scarcely a year or two older than himself. The young man was Edmund M. Blunt and in his hand he carried a copy of Moore's *Navigator*.

By the light of the yellow oil wick in Nat's tiny room began a friendship and a business association that was to last for many years.

Blunt was an enterprising book publisher from Newbury-port, up the coast from Salem. There were no copyright agreements between nations in those days, and Blunt had pirated the English edition of Moore's *Navigator* and was printing it in America. Sales were very low and for good reason. Any mariner who could be talked into buying a copy of the book and then used it generally wound up in grave difficulties. Blunt had heard of the mathematical genius of Nathaniel Bowditch and had come to see him and try to arrange with him to find out what was wrong.

Nat knew what the trouble was. He had examined Moore's book. There were two problems. First, the procedure given for taking lunar sights to calculate longitude was so faulty as to be nearly worthless. Secondly, there were not enough tables, and even more seriously, those that did exist were little more than masses of errors, so carelessly had the calculations been done.

Nat explained the difficulties to Blunt. More tables would have to be added; a better system for lunars would have to be included, and lastly, every single set of figures that Moore offered would have to be recalculated. The job would take years. He was willing to undertake the task, but there were problems . . .

Moore brushed aside the objections and offered a solution. "Let's not," he said, "add any more tables. Let's not include your system for lunars. Instead, just correct what you can of Moore's tables. As many as you have time for."

"The book will still be faulty. And inadequate," said Nat.

"I know, but it'll be a start. Better'n nothing," said Blunt. Then he made a further suggestion.

Blunt knew that a poor man cannot write a book unless he has an income. Although he was not rich by any means, he had faith in Nat and such a belief in the need for a good book on navigation that he was willing to advance enough cash money to finance the work.

This did it. Nat undertook the job. He was probably the only man in America who could have been entrusted with such a task, and he was overjoyed. For the first time in his life, he was going to be *paid,* even though the amount was small, for doing something he believed in and really knew how to do.

Next evening Nat rang the bell at the Boardman mansion with unaccustomed assurance. After dinner he spoke of his good news.

"Oh, Nat," said Elizabeth, her eyes shining, "now you have an income."

He nodded modestly. "Yes indeed. And much is possible."

Elizabeth's glance traveled slowly about the room. The crackling fireplace, the gleaming crystal of lamp chimneys, the dark old walls and pictures were all comfortable and familiar things. She didn't know why she was trembling.

Her mother looked at the two young people—her daughter, who seemed about ready to swoon, and the pale, spindly little ex-clerk for whom she felt such deep trust and affection.

"Nathaniel," Mrs. Boardman said. "Elizabeth . . . if you will excuse me for a moment . . ." The older lady left the room.

Nat was not the man to hesitate when tackling any important project. He moved to the couch beside Elizabeth and took her hand.

The *Salem Gazette* of March 25, 1798, carried the following brief announcement: "MARRIED—In this town, by the Rev. Mr. Bentley, Mr. Nathaniel Bowditch to Miss Elizabeth Boardman."

Nat packed up all his books, his few clothes, his papers, pencils, slates and notes, and moved into the home of his bride. It was a happy marriage, filled with love and kindness. Elizabeth and her mother, in the wise way of certain women, not only loved Nat deeply, but somehow they also recognized his brilliance. Both of them—Elizabeth, who was only eighteen years old, and her mother —insisted that Nat waste no time but should settle down immediately and let them take care of him. His working time, they said, should all be devoted to his mathematics and the project at hand—the revision of Moore's *Navigator*.

Upstairs in the big house a small room was fitted out as a study for him and here he plugged away at the calculations. He was happier than he'd ever been in his life, oblivious to everything but his work and the warmth and affection which surrounded him.

Not completely oblivious. Once again he was having money troubles. The stipend Blunt paid him was very small and even though there was all he needed in the Boardman household, his pride drove him very hard. As "head of the family" he insisted on contributing largely to its support, which meant he had to use the profits he had made on the *Astrea*. They could not last forever.

Nat was an excellent mathematician, but like many a

man before him, and since, he was less than accurate when it came to calculating the cost of running a home. Bowditch had to face the bitter truth—the money would soon be gone.

The only way he could possibly earn another large amount of money was to make another trip to sea. The chance came almost immediately.

American merchants and ships were making fortunes out of the misfortunes of Europe. This was during the worst days of the Napoleonic Wars, when the French and their allies were seriously challenging England's position as mistress of the seas. It was just a few years later, in 1805, during the climax of these wars between France and Britain, that Admiral Horatio Nelson defeated the combined fleets of France and England at the famed battle of Trafalgar and made the seas safe again for British shipping.

In the meantime, neutral nations, such as the little United States of America, were doing a rush-order business supplying foods and manufactured goods to both the belligerents. The shipping lanes were hazardous; to be caught by the French meant confiscation for ship and cargo and imprisonment for the crew.

The *Astrea* was just the ship for such a perilous voyage. She was big, heavily armed, and fast. Derby decided to send her to Spain and chose Prince to command her and Nathaniel Bowditch as second mate and supercargo.

On August 21, 1798, the *Astrea* cleared Salem for Cádiz. Bowditch's family had no complaints. Elizabeth and her mother were women from a long tradition. Their men were mariners, and they knew what this meant. They simply stayed behind and waited: sometimes the ships and men returned soon, but more often months or years would pass before they were home again.

Nat stood at the taffrail of the *Astrea* and gazed astern at the swiftly vanishing shoreline of home. He was happy at the chance to recover his finances and he was happy also at the thought of having weeks and weeks of free time to work without interruptions on his revisions of Moore's book. His heart however, was heavy and sad for another reason. When he kissed his bride of only five months good-by, it was with deep foreboding. Elizabeth was seriously ill, and her malady had been diagnosed as consumption.

Eleven

The *Astrea* returned to Salem in the spring of 1799, about nine months after she had left. For Nat Bowditch this period was a time of grinding work and of nearly unbearable personal sorrow.

The ship's first port of call was Cádiz, on the Atlantic coast of Spain. By now there was no question about who did the navigating on the *Astrea*. Nat laid out a departure course for Prince when they cleared Salem and continued to make the daily fixes which guided them safely all the way across. In addition to this work, Nat forced himself to bury his worries about Elizabeth in the back of his mind and to plunge resolutely into the task of going over the calculations in Moore's tables.

The task was monumental. Day after day, day after weary day, Nat kept at it with pencil and slate, meticulously working his way through the complex mathematics from which the simple figures in the tables were derived. And at nighttime too, he continued to work by the light of the wavering whale oil lamp until his eyes felt ready to pop from his head.

From Cádiz the ship headed south toward the Strait of Gibraltar for a run into the Mediterranean and the port of Alicante on the southern coast of Spain. The "gut," as the strait was called by sailors in those times, was literally swarming with heavily armed warships and privateers flying the banners of Spain, France, and England. These heavily armed belligerents were sparring constantly as they jockeyed to corner enemy ships. Any sail could represent a potential antagonist and the nerves of everybody concerned were stretched tight with the tension. This was no place for a peaceful merchantman from a neutral nation, and time and again the *Astrea* had to submit to search by suspicious boarding crews, or to pipe all hands on the double to the guns when it seemed as though she might have to fight.

At other times she traveled in convoys of merchantmen cluttered together like chicks for mutual comfort. Because of her speed and weight of armament and superior navigation, the *Astrea* frequently acted as mother hen, even occasionally putting over a line to slower ships and hurrying them along with a tow.

In spite of the constant turmoil and danger, Nat kept at his calculations. His action station was an ignominious one, but under the circumstances Prince cannot be blamed for getting his frail little navigator out of the way. Cannon need to be served by fighting men, not mathematicians. Nat was assigned to be the "powder monkey," a post usually reserved for the young boys of a ship's crew. His job was to rush powder from the magazine to the guns as it was needed. In all truth, while this was not a real "action" job, it was nerve-wracking. He had to wait below decks, unable to see anything of what was going on, surrounded by gunpowder. It was no place for a jittery man, but Nat was calm, and probably would have methodically performed his task with a minimum of fuss had the ship ever gone into action.

Luckily his ability as a powder monkey was not put to a test. The *Astrea* never had to fight, but there were some close calls. One evening, in the light of a full moon, she was beating her way along with several other armed ships toward Alicante, and a strange sail was sighted bearing down on them. Prince immediately got his ship ready for action. The stranger turned out to be an English frigate who did not bother them. She sheared off toward Gibraltar. In the relaxation that followed, Bowditch was forgotten for several hours.

When Prince missed Nat, he hurried below to the magazine to see what had happened. Looking down the hatch, he burst into a roar of laughter.

By the light of a dim battle lantern he saw Nat happily perched on a barrel of gunpowder, slate on his knees, pencil in hand, the picture of tranquillity. Throughout all the excitement and furor of the alarm he had been working out calculations for Moore's tables.

In Alicante, Nat's darkest fears for Elizabeth were realized. He received word in a very roundabout manner from other American ships in the harbor that she had died. In vain he awaited confirmation or letters which would have given him details of her death. Nothing came. He was not well-liked in Salem, and something of his status is revealed by his journal. Heartsick and lonely, he wrote: ". . . none of my friends in Salem have seen fit to give me details of the death of my beloved wife."

Homeward bound at last, Nat buried his grief in more and more work, determined to finish as much of the task as he could.

Prince clattered down the ladder from the poop deck to the saloon. The ship was nearing the coast of America; it was late at night, cold and stormy. He stood silently, a dark figure in dripping oilskins, swaying back and forth as he balanced himself against the rolling and pitching of the *Astrea*.

Prince looked down at the table. There, in the dim light of the oil wick, Nat was fast asleep, his head buried on his crossed arms in a confused mass of cluttered papers. Disturbed, Nat looked up, his eyes blinking sleepily.

Prince grinned. "Pretty late, Nat," he said. "And you look about as tired as you could be and still be alive."

Nat yawned in utter weariness. He nodded.

"More mistakes?" asked Prince.

"Uh . . . huh," said Nat.

"How many black marks now against Johnny Moore?" asked Prince. This was the standard joke between them. Every mistake Nat found was a "black mark against Johnny Moore."

Nat shook his head in disbelief. "I don't know . . . I've just about lost track." He fumbled in the notebook, squinted at it. "No wonder sailors can't abide arithmetic

[146]

navigation. Any man trusting this book would be sure to go ashore." He tapped Moore's *Navigator* in derision.

"How many, Nat?" prodded Prince.

"You'll never believe it, Henry," said Nat disgustedly. "Almost six thousand so far, and I'm nowhere near done."

Prince's jaw fell. He looked more carefully at Nat. No wonder the little supercargo looked on his last legs, especially since, as Prince well knew, each one of those mistakes was like a stab to the heart for Nat because it made light of something that was sacred to him, caused people to mistrust that which could be trusted.

"And any one of those mistakes could drive a ship ashore if it was applied near a coastline. No wonder people laugh at celestial navigation."

"But now it's all right? Now the mistakes are corrected?"

Nat shook his head. "I figure I'll get about eight thousand before Blunt starts hollering for the book. And that won't be nearly all of 'em, Henry. I just don't have time. And even then the book won't be any good. There are still too many mistakes I won't catch. Tables still too scanty. His method of working lunars no good." Nat sniffed in disgust. "No. No. This mess is not the answer. Never will be."

He sighed, gathered up the papers, took them to his cabin. Then, rubbing the sleep from his eyes, he took his sextant from its case and started for the ladder to the poop deck. He said briskly, "Let's take some lunars ourselves the right way. No use piling the *Astrea* on the coast now we're so close to home."

Halfway up the ladder he turned and spoke to Prince

again. "Bring your watch will you? Maybe we can use the thing to help us. I've thought of a way if maybe we averaged out its loss and then . . ." Nat's voice dwindled as he vanished into moon and starlit night above them.

Back home in Salem Nat continued to live with Elizabeth's mother, Mrs. Boardman. The huge house was lonely for the old lady. She enjoyed taking care of him, and like her dead daughter she had an abiding faith in his genius and what he was trying to do.

Nat returned to her all the things which Elizabeth had brought to her marriage as a dowry. He felt that he had not been married to Elizabeth long enough to have any claim on them. The silver plate, the linen, the glassware, and all the other items which girls in those days considered a proper dowry were carefully packed and given back to Mrs. Boardman.

The corrections of Moore's *Navigator* were finished and turned over to Blunt. Nat had been right. He wound up with about "eight thousand black marks against Johnny Moore." The book was scheduled for publication in September 1799. When it came out, Nat's name was not even on the title page, and he probably was relieved. A reference was merely made to certain revisions by a skillful "mathematician and navigator." He and Blunt looked forward to still another edition, and they laid plans for Nat to continue to revise the work.

In his study upstairs in the Boardman mansion, Nat wearily set to the task, but his heart wasn't in it. He was crushed by the death of Elizabeth . . . "a momentary vision of bliss which had flitted before him and vanished forever." He had come to loathe working on Moore. The continual calculating and revising was a job which lay like a stone on his heart. There was nothing in it of his own and even when he had completely overhauled it, it would still be so far short of what such a work should have been that he felt he was working at a futile task. Nevertheless he kept at it. The future seemed black and hopeless, but there was nothing else for him to do.

There were a few rays of light to cheer him, however. Although his true ability was recognized only by Captain Henry Prince, his genius began to be accepted, even though moderately, in certain circles.

He became a member of the Philosophical Society in Salem and thus had permanent access to the books of Richard Kirwan which he had so avidly devoured years before. He was also elected to the American Academy of Arts and Sciences. Nat was pleased to receive this honor, but he was not taken in by it. In those days, with a few exceptions, American scientists were simple, practical men in comparison to those in the Old World, who were far ahead of anything in science on this side of the Atlantic. European societies were publishing papers on gravity, biology, astronomy, and were beginning to probe tentatively into such unlikely phenomena as electricity. European scientists and mathematicians were delving into the darkest secrets of the heavens and the earth. Their speculations were of the highest order. Americans at this time were more concerned with the development of their new land, and their "scientific" articles were apt to deal with such matters as a better way to refine whale oil, or advice to housewives on how to make soap! Nat knew about this difference; he suffered much from his lack of contact with other men as learned as himself. Nevertheless, he accepted his election to the American Academy happily, even though to his honest way of thinking, it probably was a pretty hollow honor.

And so he settled down as best he could, doggedly going to work to correct somebody else's book. Wearily he hoped for something to change, not knowing at all what it would be. The opportunity came sooner than he expected. By July 1799, after a little more than three months ashore, he was back at sea again.

Old Elias Hasket Derby was at long last seriously ill. The gout, apoplexy, and other ailments had finally brought even this tough old warrior to a halt. He felt himself at the brink of death, as indeed he was.

One of his last acts was to sell the *Astrea* to a firm of Boston shipowners. By now the beautiful ship was famous for her fast passages. The new owners did not know the reason for these quick voyages, but of one thing they were sure: they wanted her officers to make at least one trip in her under their ownership. They were highly impressed with the profits made when the ship went to Manila on the first voyage, and so they scheduled a second trip to that port for her. Prince and Bowditch were happy to oblige. A temporary crew was signed, and they took the *Astrea* up to Boston for loading. By July they were ready once again to sail for the Philippines.

By now the saloon of the *Astrea* was like home to both Prince and Nat. They sat at the table the day before they were to sail, making plans. The polished mahogany of the sideboard with its gleaming mirror and silver and brasswork shone brightly along the port side. The walnut of the table and the inlaid rose and cherrywood of the bulk-

heads were lightly oiled and picked up the glow of the
afternoon sun which filtered down the skylight. The supercargo and Captain Prince were relaxed in the beautiful
cabin, content, talking over the voyage. Nat had a calendar
before him. He looked up at Prince.

"When do you plan to sail?" he asked.

"Immediately. Tomorrow if we can get away," said
Prince.

Nat did some brief calculating. "Have you figured
when that will put us in the Indian Ocean?"

The cabin steward, a young boy named Charley Waldo,
came in with coffee. The pot was of pure, gleaming silver,
the cups and saucers were delicate and beautiful French
china. The set had been a present from Elias Derby to
the officers of his favorite ship. Charley was very happy
to be sailing on a ship with officers who were famed for
their fast passages. He felt he might learn something,
and indeed, he may have, because in later years he became a famous sailing master in the United States Navy.

Now he served the coffee and hung about, fussing at the
sideboard, trying to overhear what these two were saying.
He had heard stories about each of them, but he could not
make up his mind what to believe. Certainly Captain
Henry Prince looked every inch a seaman. The scrawny,
short, domed-foreheaded supercargo, Nathaniel Bowditch,
wasn't very impressive, but then there were stories about
him, too, and his wizardry with a sextant. Charley strained
his ears.

Prince noticed the boy and dismissed him with a frown
and a curt order. Sailing plans for the ship, which he and
Nat were discussing, were of no concern to the cabin
boy.

"Yes," he said, "I know when we'll get there."

"Then where," said Nat, "will you wait for the monsoon shift?"

"We won't wait. We'll take her to Manila in the face of the monsoon."

For a moment neither spoke. Each was deep in thought. Nat was incredulous. Such a passage was squarely against all tradition and dogma of the times.

Prince nodded slowly. "Yes. Through the Indies clear to Manila."

Nat thought of the endless miles of unknown waters, of the pathetic charts available to them. Then Prince continued.

"I want to try it. It's never been done before," he said. He looked at Nat squarely. "Nat, can you do it?"

Nat laughed. "*I?* Henry, *I* can't do it. I can tell you where the ship is, all right. But you know those charts. *You'll* have to sail her." Nat had long ago given up any idea that he was a bucko shipmaster.

Prince grinned. "Leave that part of it to me, Nat. You stick to the stars and your sextant. With luck we'll be back in a year."

They drank their coffee and proceeded to make plans. All unknown to them, a young man in a buggy was raising a cloud of dust and whipping his horse as he raced like mad toward Boston. He drove all that night and sighed in relief as he tore into the town in the morning. The *Astrea* had not yet cleared but had left the dock and was swinging tranquilly on her cable at the anchorage waiting for the afternoon tide and wind.

He hired a boatman to row him out to the ship. No visitors were expected; the *Astrea* was ready for sea, already cut off from the land. An obliging sailor tossed over a Jacob's ladder and the man clambered aboard. It was Edmund Blunt.

Below in the saloon Blunt offered his apologies to Captain Prince for coming aboard at such an unusual time. Prince nodded in grave pardon and signaled, like a gracious host, to Charley Waldo for more coffee. Then he rose to leave, politely offering Nat and Blunt the opportunity to discuss their business in private. Nat indicated that Prince should stay. They would talk about nothing so important that the master of the ship would have to get out of his own dining saloon.

Blunt and Nat talked a long, long time. Prince kept out of it, but gradually a smile spread across his face as he listened.

Blunt had a brand-new idea. Nat should do no more revisions on Moore's *Practical Navigator*. Instead, he should start from scratch and do a new book, a book all his own. Blunt was convinced of Nat's genius, and further-more he believed that the time was absolutely ripe for a real book, a *true* practical book on celestial navigation.

He brushed aside Nat's cautious objections. "Yes, yes, I know," he said. "I know mariners mistrust celestial navigation. And with good reason. Books like Moore's. But yours they will be able to trust implicitly. And you know the subject. Maybe better than anyone else in the world. Isn't that right, Captain?" He looked at Prince.

Prince nodded, smiling gravely. Nobody had to tell *him* that Nat Bowditch could navigate a ship.

"So write it down," continued Blunt. "Put everything in it. Everything from beginning to end. As you think it should be. In your own words. Your own planning. Organize it yourself and we'll publish it in your name. It'll be *your* book. Your tables. Your lunar method."

Blunt's enthusiasm was catching. In a moment the two men were shaking hands, Nat grinning happily. This was really something important.

Prince stirred uneasily in his chair. Up through the hull of his ship, he had caught the movement, the vibrations of the turning tide as it began to run seaward. He could sense the *Astrea* swinging. He rose, held out his hand to Blunt, and grinned.

"Now, Mr. Blunt," he said. "Will you get off my ship? We've a long voyage ahead of us. Nat here will need every minute he can find."

After wishing them a safe and prosperous voyage, Blunt climbed down the side of the *Astrea*. He plumped himself in the stern of the skiff and headed for shore.

The sails were loosed, the anchor weighed. With the tide and a soft afternoon breeze, the big vessel slowly gathered way and glided out to sea. Nat's last glimpse was of Blunt waving good-by from the rowboat.

That very same night, after laying out the departure course for Prince, Nat summoned up all his enthusiasm and resolutely set to work.

He had a fantastic task ahead of him. One that would take years to complete.

Twelve

Hard on the port tack, under shortened sail, the *Astrea* drove over a confused, leaden sea. She wallowed, yawed, rolled, pitched. Rigging and spars slatted and banged; her woodwork creaked and groaned as the strains on the laboring ship seemed to come from every which direction at once.

Every man jack aboard was jumpy and nervous. These were not seas to gladden a sailor's heart. They were not the seas which rolled steadily on the wide vast ocean. These were seas reflected from the bottom, in shoal water, from unseen reefs, unseen islands, every one of them almost sure death to any vessel that scraped them.

Captain Prince paced the poop deck, worry in every line of his face. He gazed at the crew gathered in little knots along the length of the *Astrea* and at the men clustered about the anchor windlass on the foc'sle head. He could feel their tension and didn't blame them. These were not waters to inspire confidence in deep-sea sailors.

He gazed upward. The lookout stood high above them all on the foremast, standing on the topmast yard, steadying himself with his arm about the slender truck.

"Ahoy aloft," Prince roared. "What ho?"

"Nothing, Captain, except that the water seems to be shoaling on the starboard side."

"Keep a sharp eye now," said Prince.

"Aye, sir," the man said. As if anybody had to tell him, he thought.

Prince gave a brief order to the helmsman, who spun the big wheel a few spokes. The bow of the *Astrea* eased very gently a point or two away from the possible shoal reported by the lookout.

"Rain squall on the starboard, Captain." The voice of the lookout floated down from his sky-scraping perch on the mast.

Prince cursed beneath his breath, examined the horizon with his glass. Sure enough, he could see it coming. A heavy, black, oily cloud boiled ever higher into the sky, and beneath it, like water spilling from a punctured balloon, he saw the sheets and waves of falling rain.

Soon the squall was upon the ship. The lookout peered even more uneasily about him. The water far below was pocked and pitted now with the rain. All visibility was wiped out by the streaming sheets of water. The ship continued to move along like a tormented ghost, a lost and abandoned spirit of the sea. The lookout scrubbed the water from his eyes but still could see nothing. It was as though he floated through a silvery bubble, far above the dimpled sea surface.

Without an order, the hands on deck moved to the proper braces and halyards of the few sails that were set. The carpenter on the foc'sle head picked up his ax, standing by the ropes that secured the anchor cable. These were seawise, shipwise men. They knew ahead of time what the orders would be if trouble came.

The lookout on the foremast strained even more sharply. Was that a rumble, a strange hiss coming to him on the wind? He couldn't know but he muttered a brief plea to the gods of the sea to halt the rain, if but for a moment.

The straining ship drove on.

Suddenly the lookout's prayer was answered. The rain eased slightly, the cloud passed, and he was out of it.

The hairs on his neck bristled. Dead ahead was that which honest sailors feared more than any other thing. Breakers!

"White water. White water dead ahead," he screamed.

Prince didn't hesitate, nor in this emergency did he speak his order quietly to his anxious first mate standing beside him. He bellowed himself with all the power of his lungs.

"Let go, let go!"

The words were scarcely out of his mouth when the carpenter's ax slashed downward, cutting the ropes holding the anchor and cable. It roared through the hawsepipe, plunging toward bottom.

"Give her five fathoms," Prince bellowed.

Then the orders came thick and fast, and so quickly did the men respond it seemed they were even ahead of the captain.

"Hard alee. Hard alee at the wheel." The helmsman spun the wheel hard over; the head of the ship slowly began coming around, up into the wind.

"Let go the port braces." The cook, at his traditional spot on the lee braces, let them fly.

"Man the weather braces. A long hard pull. Move. MOVE FAST now, you lubbers," roared Prince.

The braces, which are exactly what the name implies, lines which are attached to the spars of a square-rigger and which brace the spars and their sails to the proper angle to the wind, were manhandled by the men.

As the cook let the lee braces fly, those on the weather side ran them in, that is, they didn't haul them hand over hand, but actually ran with the lines, to send the yards flying about. First the mizzen mast, then the main, then the foremast. So fast did the men run that in very short order the sails were all aback, with the wind pressing on their forward sides. The effect was to slow the ship, to drive her astern.

Prince had felt the anchor hit bottom, even through the confusion of running men, flapping canvas, and squealing blocks in the rigging. The anchor crew let five fathoms, or thirty feet, run out; then the mate, on the foc'sle, said, "Hold her."

Prince thanked his stars for an honest, stout Salem anchor. The flukes dug deep into the bottom as the men applied the brakes on the windlass, holding the flying cable.

The anchor gouged through the sand, flukes seeking a hard grip. The men on the ship could feel the vibrations coming up the cable. Finally the anchor held solid, the cable trembling with the strain. The carpenter on the

[158]

windlass eased the brake gently, giving the cable a bit more scope, trying to relieve some of the strain.

Under the pressure of the wind on the backed sails and the drag of the anchor, the *Astrea* began grinding to a stop. But on she went, ever more slowly, as the carpenter played with the brake. He kept enough strain to get maximum drag and at the same time stay just under the snapping point.

It is not easy, in fact it is not possible, to stop a heavily laden ship in her own tracks. The momentum of the great tonnage of the *Astrea* pulled her along forward, as she pitched and slewed and began dragging to a stop. Prince gazed aloft to where the lookout watched with horror as the creaming line of reef came closer, and he ground his teeth with the tension. They'd be lucky not to pull every stick right out of her in a stop like this. Rigging and masts were not made for such treatment. The ship trembled throughout her long length, quivering. Shrouds, stays, spars, even the lofty masts themselves snapped and jerked.

Everything miraculously held, however, and the *Astrea* slowed to a stop, shaking and trembling like a spent racehorse.

Prince and the crew had time now to look about them. Ahead, not fifty yards distant and in clear sunshine, the sea hissed and tumbled over a long low line of coral reef. Its sharp and jagged teeth, visible occasionally in the hollows of the swells, could have torn the bottom right out of the *Astrea* had she piled on them.

Prince gave the necessary orders. The anchor was heaved in, pulling the ship backward. The sails were trimmed again to the wind and the ship paid off on a new course to the north, a few miles off the reef and running parallel to it.

He wiped his face with his handkerchief. His forehead was wet, not with drops of rain so much as with the sweat of very real fear. Once again the *Astrea* had been saved by luck and lightning fast seamanship. He was conscious of hostile glances from the crew and of their angry, sullen muttering. He couldn't blame them. He glanced at the reef; no captain had a right to risk his ship and the lives of the men in her in such a manner. Turning the vessel over to the first mate, he went below.

Nat Bowditch was sitting quietly at the table in the saloon, working on his book, calculating endlessly, as it seemed to Prince, he had been doing for months.

Bowditch looked up. "Another reef?" he asked quietly.

Prince's jaw set. He didn't trust himself to speak at this moment. He strode to the sideboard, poured half a tumbler of rum in a glass and swallowed it in two gulps.

"Yes, Nat," he said, "another reef." Then he again asked the question he'd asked a dozen times before. "Nat, where in the devil are we?"

Nat stopped his scribbling on the slate, picked up the chart, gazed silently a moment and then looked at Prince, something like a wise little owl. He gave him some figures. So many degrees of latitude and so many degrees of longitude.

Prince poured himself a bit more rum, tossed it off, then said angrily, "Arithmetic. Numbers. Figures. Nat, that's what you deal in. I've got a ship and a crew and a cargo. And a bad reef out there. That's what *I* have to deal in."

Nat said mildly, "I know that, Henry. But we *are*

exactly where I told you. I can't help it if not a chart aboard this ship is correct . . . if they don't show a reef at our present position." Nat's disgust grew. "Inaccuracy!! It's the curse of sailors."

Under the warm spread of the rum, Prince's good humor returned. "Yes, I know you're right, Nat. But, my God, how long can this go on? One of these times we won't make it."

Nat just looked at Captain Prince and shrugged his shoulders.

"All right, go ahead, go ahead," said Prince. "Mark the reef in on the chart. Maybe it'll save some other poor devil. Here, look." He traced the reef out for Nat with his finger. "About north by east it runs. Maybe five hundred yards long and looks to be half a mile wide."

Nat carefully penciled it in on the chart.

Said Prince, "But there's another thing, Nat. The hands are restless. And I can't blame 'em. They're at the end of their rope. None of 'em have had a full night's sleep in months. Watch and watch and half the time not even that. Watch all the time. They're asleep on their feet."

It was true. Months ago, it seemed, the deep blue waters of the South Atlantic and of the Indian Ocean had been left behind. The ship had worked her way through Sunda Strait into the shoaling green of the island waters of the Indies. Straight into the teeth of the monsoon she had gone, tacking day and night, month after month, clawing her way, fighting for each mile, toward Manila. She struggled through unknown waters, past cannibal islands, past the strongholds of slavers, threading her way through rocks, submerged reefs. Time after time the anchor had been let fly on the run, or the sails trimmed about in the nick of time to save her. And all this in the face of the adverse monsoon, the captain disdaining to wait for the fair wind which the good Lord himself had provided to blow simple mariners safely and accurately to their destinations.

And perhaps worst of all for the hands, nobody really knew where the ship was except Nat Bowditch, the scrawny supercargo who could not be trusted even to stand a proper watch. When he was asked where the ship was, all he could give was some numbers, some arithmetic!

Prince continued. "I mean it, Nat. The men are about full of it. All they can stand. They're wrecks from too many watches. Too many brushes with real *death,* not brushes with mathematics. We'll be lucky if we don't have a mutiny. They want to get back safely to their families. Not drowned on some forsaken coral spit."

Nat seemed to change the subject. "Henry," he said, "how many of the man forward would you consider officer material?"

"*What?*" Prince was astounded. "I don't know," he muttered. "Maybe half. Maybe all. They're good Boston men and no doubt hope for commands of their own. Except maybe some of the old shellbacks. What are you getting at?"

Nat said, "My methods are right. They work. The tables are coming along. One thing, though, I'm not sure of." Nat nodded to himself in perplexity and then seemed to come to a decision. "I've got to be certain that anybody, I mean *anybody,* Henry, can navigate with my system. Men like you've got forward."

"So?" queried Prince curiously.

"So I'm going to try an experiment. Teach every man

[162]

aboard to navigate. Even the cook. Take lunars, use the sextant, logarithms, the tables. The whole works. If I can't make them understand it, then the whole book's a farce."

"Well, I'll be . . ." Prince muttered.

"That's right. Everybody. And furthermore, once they get the idea and can work up daily positions, they won't be so nearly mutinous, as you call it, although I think you're exaggerating."

Prince roared in laughter. "Nat, you've got men there who scarcely know their sums. But they're *sailors*. They know when a ship is in trouble. As this one is. And you're going to calm 'em down by teaching them mathematics?"

"Yes," said Nat, with emphasis.

So the *Astrea* struggled on toward Manila, saved time and time again by nothing more than the superb seamanship of Captain Prince and his crew. But now there was a difference, as Nat had known there would be.

Nat held daily classes. He undertook to teach every man jack on the *Astrea* how to navigate. These were the men who would be commanding ships, and navigating them, in the future. They *had* to learn if there was any validity in what he was writing. The complicated processes were simplified. Even the most fumbling old salts, men who could scarcely keep addition and subtraction clear in their heads, were challenges, and were taught the basic principles of celestial navigation.

Classes were held on deck. Diagrams and computations were done on the holystoned planks. Daily positions were worked out. The charts were explained, their deficiencies noted. With infinite patience Nat taught the men how to use a sextant, how to take sun sights, how to take the delicate lunar observations. Ever and ever Nat continued to simplify. The questions of the men clarified his own thinking, sharpened his explanations.

As the voyage wore on the men did learn to navigate! It was quite unbelievable and a miracle to Prince. Only when every man aboard could work up the necessary sights —from the cabin boy up—was Nat satisfied. *Now* he knew that the principles of celestial navigation could be learned by anyone, if properly taught, and that any seaman could make daily fixes quickly and accurately.

And he was right about the men in another way too. As the ship labored onward into the wind through dangerous waters, the attitude aboard toward him changed. A whole new world had opened up for the hands. They began to see that arithmetic seamanship was in its way a pretty great thing. They began to believe in their figures. Blame for the ship's troubles was no longer placed on Nat but on the charts, where it belonged, and the men clucked in derision at the inaccuracies.

Eventually the horrors of the voyage through the complex of the Indies were left behind. The dark, forbidding coasts of New Guinea and Borneo were only memories. The Philippines lay ahead; the last "Land O" rang from the masthead. Quickly Prince made the run down the coast to Manila, and the anchor was let fly in the pale green waters of the bay.

The ship claimed the impossible—a run through the Indies in the face of the monsoon. The astounded people of Manila could scarcely believe the story, but there was no disputing the evidence as she lay calmly swinging on her anchor.

Soon the *Astrea*'s men were local sensations and the

pride of the handful of Americans living in the city. It was conceded that there was "more knowledge of navigation on board the *Astrea* than there ever was on all the ships that had floated on Manila Bay." It was Captain Prince's proud boast that every jack tar on his ship could take a lunar sight and work up a position as well as "Sir Isaac Newton were he still alive."

Trading was soon completed; the big ship was deep with her return cargo—spices, hides, and indigo. The flabbergasted Manilans were now due for another shock. Any ordinary ship would have settled down to wait six months for the shift in the monsoon. The *Astrea* was no ordinary ship; one fine morning her crew of learned mathematicians loosed the sails, weighed the anchor, and headed for home, straight in the teeth of the wind.

The run through the Indies was made in good time. Soon the ship was swaying freely with the deep, powerful swells of the Indian Ocean beneath her keel. The Cape of Good Hope ghosted past them, and there was nothing between the ship and home but the vast South Atlantic. The run was completed without incident except for a very bad leak that developed. Somehow the *Astrea* had sprung the calking from a long seam, and the crew was kept pumping day and night for weeks on end.

They sailed into Boston Harbor in September 1800, approximately fourteen months after they had left. The people of Boston, and the owners, were incredulous. In spite of the pleas of the owners, Nat and Captain Prince both left the ship to go home to Salem. At the venerable age of thirty-five, Prince was determined on retirement. He had his big fine house ready and waiting, all stocked with good port wine, Havana cigars and mementoes of his voyages. Nat still had years of work to do on his book.

Nat settled down to what must have been one of the most miserable periods of his life. In spite of all he had done and contributed to celestial navigation, he was still considered the inept, almost comical, arithmetic sailor. After this last voyage of the *Astrea,* he had thought perhaps that things might be a bit different, but he was condemned to disappointment. People were not yet ready to accept him.

All he could do was to settle down to a day and night grind to finish the book. In addition to the text, the explanations and the diagrams, the thousands upon thousands of extremely complicated computations for the tables drained all his strength and time. This was long before any such thing as a mechanical calculator, so every formula had to be made laboriously on the slate. Since he was determined that above all, *his* book should be accurate, he worked each set of figures three times.

There were two bright rays in the endless chore of work. One was that he had returned with a fair amount of money from the *Astrea,* and so his eternal penury was somewhat lessened. He had enough capital now to begin to take part in various business ventures of the port. He put some money in a West Indian trading schooner and profited handsomely. He invested also in a sealing expedition to the South Atlantic and nearly lost his shirt! By and large though, he was successful in his ventures.

The other bright spot in his lonely life was that he had remarried. This time his wife was Mary Ingersoll, a fine, lovely country girl who loved Nat with all her heart. In the way of the times, when all Salem families seemed to be connected in one manner or another, she was Nat's first cousin, as well as being the second cousin of his first wife! She was an excellent spouse, and like poor Elizabeth Boardman before her, she believed in Nat and in what he was trying to do, standing up for him in the face of the scoffing in the town.

At long last, two years later, in 1802, the last calculation was done for the book and meticulously checked. The last paragraph of explanations had been written, the last maps and diagrams completed. Nat called the book the *New American Practical Navigator.* Blunt took one look at the manuscript and recognized instantly the value of what he held in his hands. He decided on a bold course of action.

He sailed to London and took the book to the very same publishers from whom he had previously pirated Moore's *Navigator.* These staid and conservative gentlemen were understandably quite cool, if not downright hostile, to the brash young man from America and his manuscript. Blunt prevailed upon them at least to look it over, and when they did, their attitude changed completely. Here at last was the book that ought to revolutionize the subject of marine navigation. They agreed to bring it out.

The *New American Practical Navigator,* by Nathaniel Bowditch, appeared in print in Boston in June 1802, simultaneously with the English edition. Except for a ripple of interest in British naval and merchant shipping circles, the book caused hardly a stir in the maritime world. In America, a few of the younger, more progressive captains, took a quick look and decided that possibly there might be something to it . . . that is, if they ever had time to get at it! The older shipmasters and owners were not the least impressed.

In the world of scholars and that of mathematicians, however, the reception was different. The genius of its author was recognized immediately. Bowditch was made a member of a number of very dignified scientific societies in Europe. At home, Harvard University offered him a degree, which he accepted, and a chair to teach mathematics, which he refused.

Heartsick, Nat watched what was happening. More than honors, more than degrees or teaching jobs, he wanted his book to be used and accepted by those for whom it was intended: the mariners who took the lovely square-riggers to sea. It was not. Old ways die hard, in spite of the need for new. The sailors of Salem and of the rest of the world could take or leave the *New American Practical Navigator*. What could have been a time of joy and of vindication for its author, was instead a time of dullness, filled with the salt of bitterness. The years of toil, the labor of night after night had brought but small results.

Except for his family, Nat still had few friends in Salem, and no intimates. His life became ever more lonely. Nothing brought any satisfaction except his continued work in astronomy. He did a series of brilliant and authoritative articles on the paths of comets and other heavenly bodies. He began a translation of the monumental work by Pierre Simon Laplace, the so-called "Newton of France," to make *Mécanique Céleste* available to the English-speaking world.

So, doggedly continuing his work, in the face of disappointment and frustration, and his old plague—mounting financial difficulties—Nat kept hoping against hope that something would change. This break came sooner than he expected.

Thirteen

Captain Jonathan Carnes was as bucko a young mate and skipper as Salem ever produced. Tall, powerful, daring, he was known as a man who could take a ship anywhere and get her home safely. The story is told how at one time when leaving a foreign port during a storm, young Captain Carnes found that the bar at the mouth of the harbor was too shallow for his ship. He retreated, reballasted his vessel and then sailed her across the bar on her side, drawing less water than he would have upright on an even keel!

In 1793 Captain Carnes was in Benkulen, on the island of Sumatra. Along the waterfront he heard a rumor that sent him scurrying back to Salem the moment he could get away.

In Salem he held a long private conference with a

friend, a merchant of the port. Between the two of them they bought and specially equipped a small but very beautiful schooner. She had towering masts, slim, fast lines, enormous sails. Carnes and his partner armed her with extremely heavy batteries of cannon along each side. They were warned that if she ever fired a broadside, the ship would probably jar to pieces and open all her seams from the recoil. Carnes said nothing to these prophets of doom but just loaded as much powder and shot as he could carry.

He also loaded gin, tobacco, iron, and dried fish for barter. After the schooner and her cargo were paid for, Carnes and the merchant were about at the end of their financial rope; whatever gold was left they loaded in the ship's strongbox. As the vessel cleared Salem and vanished over the horizon, Carnes' partner crossed his fingers, wondered if he'd been a fool.

The name of the wicked little schooner was the *Rajah*. The name had a good ring for the part of the world where she was heading.

Eighteen months later the *Rajah* returned home with a cargo of wild pepper. This cargo had cost about $18,000 and it sold for more than $150,000! The bonanza was on.

The story of black pepper is one of man's oldest romances of far places and dangerous voyages. In the time of Bowditch, and literally for thousands of years before, pepper was the glamour spice, the royalty of all spices. Pepper gave a new, exciting flavor to man's rather dull diet of meat and bread. More than this, along with salt, pepper was the great preservative for foods of all kinds. This was no small thing before the days of refrigeration and canning.

[171]

The East Indies had always been the source of the world's supply of black pepper. Long before water routes had been discovered to these islands from western nations, Arab *dhows* made the long trips there and traded for pepper to take back to Asia. The precious commodity was carried overland along the ancient "silk routes" in plodding camel caravans to the Mediterranean and then trans-shipped to Europe. Alexandria, Genoa, Venice, Aleppo, and other proud mercantile cities of the inland sea had largely been founded on a basis of pepper.

Then a terrible thing happened. The Turks captured Constantinople in the Middle Ages and closed the old caravan routes. Europe was deprived of this vital trade. Schools such as that of Prince Henry's in Portugal had been established primarily to discover, if possible, water routes to the Indies. When Vasco da Gama discovered the route, it opened up a new era for the nations of Europe. Once again they had access to the fabulous riches of the East.

Once again spices, particularly pepper, began to flow to Europe, this time by ship the whole vast distance. European ports, especially Lisbon, became the center of the world's spice trade. Even mighty Venice, now condemned by geography and history to wither away in a back corner of the Mediterranean, was forced to buy her pepper in Lisbon.

When the great European powers began their colonial expansions, the Dutch moved into the so-called spice islands of the East Indies. The people of Sumatra, Java, Bali, and many, many others lived and prospered under the horizontal orange, white, and blue stripes of Holland. The Dutch wound up largely controlling the spices of the world and went to extreme steps to protect their monopoly. For example, death was the penalty for anyone who shipped clusters of nutmeg berries out of the Indies without first dipping them in a solution to kill the seeds so they would not grow.

Benkulen, on Sumatra, was the center of distribution for pepper in the Indies. Here it was that all ships other than Dutch came to buy the spice. In 1793, in Benkulen, Jonathan Carnes made his momentous discovery. Pepper grew wild on unexplored islands to the northward and could be bought there without interference from the Dutch if a man dared the uncharted seas, the cannibals, the fierce head-hunters and the slave traders. It was an area made to order for the likes of Captain Carnes.

When he returned to Salem after his first voyage, the town exploded. When he sailed again a few days after his cargo was discharged, three fast ships had been outfitted to follow him and try to discover where he'd gotten his pungent, black gold.

Captain Carnes and his fleet little *Rajah* outsailed and eluded his pursuers. This went on for three more voyages before he was finally trailed and the secret was out. By then he didn't care. He and his partner were wealthy men.

For a brief time Salem was the most important pepper port of the world. Millions of pounds were trans-shipped each year to Europe. The trade was fantastically dangerous, however. The swift *proas* of the island natives were well-manned and able to overwhelm any ship unfortunate to run aground or find herself becalmed. Many a Salem ship left her bones bleaching on a tropic beach, her crew sold into slavery, massacred, or eaten by the people of some native rajah.

[173]

Nevertheless, the profits were enough that courageous men never were lacking to make the trip. It was on one of these voyages after wild black pepper that Nathaniel Bowditch sailed.

Samuel Page, Abel Lawrence, and Nathan Robinson were highly respected and well-to-do merchants of Salem. They were business acquaintances of Nathaniel Bowditch and had been associated with him in shipping ventures from time to time. The four of them now decided to undertake the risky business of a pepper voyage.

For the purpose they bought a small square-rigger called the *Putnam*. She was nearly new, quite fast, and heavily armed, and in their opinion just the thing for the enterprise.

Bowditch and his partners were meeting in the office back of the musty old countinghouse of Abel Lawrence. They were discussing the voyage, and most importantly, the selection of a captain for the *Putnam*.

Lawrence was a blunt but soft-spoken man. He wasted no words. "As I see it," he said, "we've got a double problem. For the *Putnam* we need the most resolute man possible. A first-rate seaman and also somebody who knows what cannon are for and who won't hesitate to use them if the time comes."

The others looked inquiringly at Lawrence. He continued. "Now," he said, "a man such as this is apt not to be too good at the trading. Nor is he likely to be too good at the navigating. Likely to be wandering about those seas for months on end. This we cannot tolerate because the *Putnam* must be back in a year or less to catch the next market peak. This is vital."

Page and Robinson nodded their heads solemnly. Lawrence helped himself to a pinch from a gleaming gold snuffbox, and everybody waited until he'd wiped his face and streaming eyes after the shattering sneeze.

Lawrence finally recovered and continued. "I propose that Mr. Bowditch go along as master. Lots of experience bartering and keeping track of cargo. And also, and I must confess I don't know how he does it, ships he is on seem to make fast voyages."

Nat was under no illusions as to his qualifications. "I'm no sailor," he said. "You all know that."

"Right," said Lawrence. "But you certainly have the other qualifications. And it's hardly necessary to point out that as master you'll be sharing in a larger percentage of the profits."

"But who'll actually sail the ship?" asked Nat, memories of the last voyage through the Indies with Prince in the old *Astrea,* passing through his mind.

Abel Lawrence was one of Nat's few friends in the town. Lawrence looked at the diminutive scholar. "Nat," he said, "you're not that helpless, but I also realize the situation. So, for the actual management of the ship in a pinch, and for the fighting if it comes to that, we'll engage the best man we can find for your second in command."

And so it was settled. Nat agreed to the arrangement, and when the *Putnam* cleared Salem, outward bound for the Indies, he was in command of her. Nat had no illusions. He was the captain of the ship, all right, but at the same time he just wasn't the man to roar an order to sailors high aloft during a gale. He was well satisfied with his first mate, a practical man who understood his business thoroughly and who furthermore had that most important ingredient in the make-up of an officer on a windjammer: the voice of a bull.

The good-bys on the dock were said without fanfare and the ship got under way for Sumatra with nothing more dramatic from Nat Bowditch than a quiet order to the first mate: "Get the ship under way, sir."

She cleared in November 1802, and Nat very quickly established a routine for himself and his ship. He did the navigating and plotting of the courses, naturally, but except in situations of actual emergency, when he would have to take command, the officers and the crew sailed the ship. He was deep in the astronomy of Laplace's *Mécanique Céleste,* and as the voyage wore on his absorption in the work became more and more concentrated. It was a demanding study but one which he loved. The translation of the book was a formidable task, and he was grateful for the long days and nights when he was free to contemplate the swing of the planets in the vast heavens above the ship and to grapple with the mathematics which charted their paths.

Finally this time of quiet and peaceful study was over. Five months after she had left Salem, the *Putnam* lay off the coast of Sumatra. These were waters so dangerous that even the study of the stars had to take second place.

The technique for pepper ships was to cruise through the islands where wild pepper was known to grow, buying from the local rajahs, or *datos,* as they went. Not only was the navigation hazardous but these minor chieftains and their people even more so, trying by every trick in the book, fair or foul, to take advantage of the ships. Contracts were made with the headmen for so much pepper at such and such a price in the slim hope that the pepper would be delivered as agreed. As it came aboard, payment was made in gold at the end of each day. Constant armed watch had to be maintained on the ship while it was anchored because it couldn't get away quickly in case of trouble. Anchored, she was helpless, tethered to the bottom, while every sail showing on the horizon or slipping swiftly around the lee of an island was a potential enemy and every puff of smoke or echo of gunfire could mean some other pepper ship nearby was in trouble and fighting for her life.

Nat cruised slowly, stopping at the most likely ports. In some of them there was no pepper. In others the available supply was cleaned out by some other ship before him. They went to islands and ports with names as strange as those in the Arabian Nights—Soosoo, Analaboo, Tangar, Tully Oas, Laboan Nadje, and others. Gradually the *Putnam* began to fill; she was lucky and managed to keep out of trouble—luckier, in fact, than she was on a later voyage with a different master and crew, when she was lost on a reef and seven of her complement massacred! At last Nat decided to leave for home. The ship wasn't completely full, but in his opinion there was little use hanging about for more. Other ships were arriving looking for pepper, and the price was being driven up; the dato with whom Nat had a contract went back on his word in favor of selling to another ship.

The *Putnam* took on wood for the galley stove, filled her water casks, and headed out of the islands. By now she had worked her slow way so deeply into the maze of the Indies that the trip out was pure misery. It took weeks for her to thread her tortuous way to the open sea. Often Nat had to order out the ship's boat to go on ahead to take soundings and lead them safely through the reefs. Other times they were half blinded by fierce rain squalls or by the noxious fumes which poured in heavy wreaths down the sides of volcanoes.

At long last the ship was out and free in the Indian Ocean. Nat laid a course for Ile de France, near the old familiar island of Bourbon where he had made his first voyage. All hands were weary and jumpy and were over-joyed to have deep, clear water beneath them once again.

On the Ile de France, or Mauritius as it is known today, the cargo was topped off with four hundred bags of coffee. Sailing over to pay a visit to Bourbon, Nat stopped and made brief calls on old friends, watered the ship again, then set a course for Salem and home. Joyously the *Putnam* swung into her homeward-bound course. Before her, rolling on the winds, were the heavy clouds of the fragrances of coffee and pepper, fragrances which have heralded the passage of a loaded Indiaman since the time sailors first dared the Far East.

The Atlantic is stormy in the winter. For four months the ship battled foul weather, gales, and mountainous seas, but the storms and the winds and the rain were to the liking of everybody aboard her. They wanted to get home; the ship was deep and heavy and needed the strong gales to drive her. Nat trusted his officers and crew. A simple order to the mate: "Drive her hard, sir," was all that was needed. The stout little ship soared northward like a homing gull.

There were no clear skies or stars for Nat to ponder now. He spent his days below in the gloomy saloon, calculating his navigation and hanging on to the table and chairs for dear life as the *Putnam* labored over the seas.

When the ship arrived off the Massachusetts coast the shore was in the grip of the worst winter blizzard anyone could remember. Great mountains of seas, regular Atlantic graybeards, rumbled down out of the north. Wind shrieked and howled. Snow and hail and sleet, mixed with thick, ghostly fog reduced visibility to nearly zero. This was a landfall dreaded by any sensible captain. Prudent masters kept well off shore in such weather, reefed-down and hove-to, waiting it out, hoping all the while that they wouldn't be dismasted or their plunging ship open her seams in her wild gyrations.

Nat Bowditch paced the poop deck. His spindly little frame was nearly smothered in oilskins. He peered out from under his sou'wester like a worried little owl whose meditations have been interrupted. He was deep in thought, and now, in such a situation, there was no question about who was the captain. Nobody but he could make the decisions which had to be made.

He took a look at the gray sky, at the solid mass of clouds streaming overhead. It seemed to him that possibly it was lightening a bit. If it was, even though only momentarily, this was what he needed. He went below, gazed briefly at the chart spread out on the table, nodded to himself, and with his sextant went back up on deck.

He had been right. The sky cleared in a small patch for a few moments. Through the murk the sun shone weakly, long enough for Nat to brace himself against the taffrail and get a quick shot. Back below, he made a few quick calculations, checked the chart again, then returned to the deck.

There was nothing bookish or ineffectual now about the captain who gave a quiet order to his first mate. "We'll come about, sir, on the starboard tack. Shortened tops'ls and jibs. The course will be west a quarter south. Have the men look alive and stand by. All hands on deck. Nobody below.

The mate gave the order to the helmsman who looked as though he couldn't believe his ears. Then he obediently spun the wheel, the shining mahogany spokes slipped smoothly past his fingers. The yards were braced, sail shortened, and as the *Putnam* came about she paid off on the new course. The wind and seas were nearly on her beam now; she wallowed and rolled as though she would tear her masts out.

The hands muttered among themselves. They were all in a hurry to get home, especially as it was Christmas day, but they wanted to get home alive, not as melancholy drowned men washing ashore on the rocks and beaches. The channel into Salem, the granite shores up and down the coast, the shoals, all made a ready and clutching graveyard for the unwary.

"Look at him," muttered somebody, gazing at the diminutive figure standing aft, peering into the drifts of snow and sleet. "Going right in. Just like it was broad daylight on a spring afternoon."

Another growled, "The Old Man's good all right. I've never seen anybody navigate a ship like he can." These sentiments were true. Nat had won the respect and affection of his men a dozen times over with his magic ability to plot positions. But then the old shellback shook his head in disbelief. "But nobody's this good. He can't even see the mast tops and he can't see ten fathoms beyond the bowsprit. We'd best be saying our prayers."

From somewhere far ahead, or perhaps it was from astern, or to starboard or to port—no one could tell for sure in the fierce blasts of wind—drifted the sad notes of a tolling bell, marking one of the shoal rocks at the Salem approaches. The sailors shuddered; the more devout moved their lips in old prayers.

Ashore, as day waned, Salem snugged down tight against the storm. Fires crackled on the hearths, candles guttered. Only in the taverns did a few hardy souls manage to be convivial, but even here the laughter was subdued. Any seafaring town in the center of such a blizzard would be solemn indeed.

Suddenly a rumor swept through Salem. It spread like wildfire, as rumors do, without help from anyone.

Two men peered anxiously into the driving snow, over the bay, hoping against hope that the rumor was not true, or that the blizzard would let up. They were clad in streaming oilskins and were heavily muffled against the cold.

Samuel Page and Nathan Robinson were worried. They knew that if the voyage of the *Putnam* had gone well, then she should be somewhere off the coast of North America. They had no way of knowing where, or when, but what worried them now, what caused the sickening waves of fear to ripple over them, was the rumor that Nathaniel Bowditch had been seen in town.

They conferred, decided to go to Abel Lawrence's home. After their numbness was chased away by a tot of hot buttered rum, Lawrence looked at his two guests and said, "And what brings you gentlemen here?"

They hated even to carry such a story but finally Robinson said, "Abel, there's a rumor that Nat Bowditch has been seen in town."

Lawrence's eyes popped. *"Bowditch?"*

The other two men just nodded. For a moment there was no sound in the room but the shriek of the wind outside and the snapping of the fire.

The three looked at each other in dismay. They didn't even have to utter their thoughts; they were all thinking the same thing. If Bowditch had indeed been seen, it was either his ghost, or himself, a miserable castaway who had somehow managed to make his way on foot to the town. In either case, the ship could only be lost.

Lawrence and his companions licked dry lips. If the *Putnam* were lost, they could well be ruined men.

Abel Lawrence rang for a servant and ordered oilskins, a heavy jacket, muffler, boots, and a sou'wester. Storm or no storm, this story had to be settled. As he was shrugging into the dirty weather gear, there was a loud knock on the door.

The three jumped. Who could possibly be out at this hour on such a night? In a moment, the servant opened the door and Nat Bowditch stepped into the room. He was thin, dead tired, dripping wet but otherwise his usual chipper self.

"Good evening, gentlemen," he said.

They stared open-mouthed at the apparition.

"I thought perhaps I'd better drop by before going home."

Somebody made a move to relieve him of his oilskins but

Nat brushed him aside. "No. No thank you. I'll only stay a moment. My family will be waiting. It's Christmas, you know."

Finally Lawrence found his voice. He croaked, "The ship. The *Putman*. Where is she?"

Nat seemed surprised. "Why . . . where did you think she might be? Tied up at Derby wharf, of course."

Lawrence could scarcely believe it. "You . . . you . . ." he said quietly. "You brought her into port in a blow like this?"

"Naturally," said Nat. He was amazed they should think otherwise. It all seemed so very simple and easy to him. "I got a good shot of the sun. Caught a glimpse of Baker Light as we entered the channel during a lull. My sextant is good. My chart of the harbor is good. The ship's compass is excellent. What more could be needed? I knew where I was every moment. Anyone could have done it by applying some simple arithmetic. Now, if you'll excuse me? My family, you understand."

With that he was gone.

Messrs. Page, Lawrence, and Robinson looked at each other in disbelief. They settled in front of the fire. It took a good many hours, and a large number of hot buttered rums to drive the chill from their bones.

Several days later the storm broke. The *Putnam*'s crew was paid off and the work of unloading the cargo began. The ship carried nearly half a million pounds of prime quality black pepper and fifty thousand pounds of coffee.

The value of the cargo made the town rejoice. It lined the pockets of the partners with gold.

Fourteen

Bowditch's feat of bringing the *Putnam* safely to port during the storm completely flabbergasted Salem. He was an overnight hero.

Never again was his "arithmetic navigation" questioned. He had proved in the most dramatic way, once and for all, that it was to be trusted. He had done what no other mariners in Salem, or for that matter in the entire world, could have done, bluster and rant though they might about the foolishness of numbers at sea.

And what of the book on which he had spent so many years of his life and so much heartbreaking labor? What happened to the *New American Practical Navigator?*

Three items were often listed as necessary in the seabag of every youngster who heard the call of the sea, said the long good-bys to his family and headed down the road to the nearest blue-water port. One was a pair of stout woolen socks knitted by his mother; one was the Bible and the other was the *New American Practical Navigator*.

The ascending order of importance was never questioned. In time the socks would wear holes and have to be discarded. The Bible in moments of peril might provide confusing answers. The book would never fail; it would lead him anywhere on earth and bring him safely and surely home again.

After his feat of bringing in the *Putnam* during the blizzard, Nat's methods were taught and avidly studied by men of the merchant marine and navies of the world. As the years passed, anyone who had sailed with Bowditch proudly boasted that he had sat at the feet of the master. Nor was he wrong. For the first time in history men could venture forth on the ocean and know exactly where they were. To a large extent Bowditch made possible the great age of American shipping. The tall clippers standing out from Canton to New England made their marvelous voyages because they were manned and navigated by men who had studied their *New American Practical Navigator*.

As much if not more than Matthew Fontaine Maury, the great American chartmaker and oceanographer, Bowditch placed all future navigators in his debt. The book was not just another treatise in celestial navigation. It was a tool, as important as sextant or compass.

Even today it is impossible to examine a first copy of this book and not feel a thrill of pride in what the little ex-clerk from Salem accomplished. In appearance the book is impressive. It is beautifully bound; its six hundred pages are still clear and legible. The copperplates and sketches are painstakingly executed, exquisite in detail. The prose is simple, precise, and to the point.

It is a vast store of information for the mariner. There are chapters on winds, currents, the obligations of an owner, the duties of a master, a dictionary of sea terms, an explanation of all possible maneuvers of square-riggers at sea, and the appropriate commands for their execution. There are sections on marine insurance, bills of lading, foreign exchange, bills of exchange.

Mathematically it is a treasure house. Never one to get excited about the complexities of mathematics, Nat takes the reader calmly and logically from simple fractions up through decimals, geometry, algebra, logarithms, and into the more involved trigonometry and calculus concepts of navigation. Along the road there are numerous side excursions into geography, astronomy, mensuration, gauging, surveying, and the like. There is even a "section to exercise the learner."

As far as the mechanics of navigation were concerned, there had never been anything like this work. It corrected existing tables and made them trustworthy for once and all. There are twenty-nine tables, and Nat carefully listed and explained how each was derived. He so much improved the standard method of calculating latitude that it might be said he devised an entirely new one.

In addition to his new method of calculating longitude by lunar sights, the only truly workable one at the time, the book also included other procedures that were completely Bowditch's. His sections on coasting, piloting, and marine surveying incorporated original tables and systems relating to the distance of visibility of objects at sea, and are still in use.

Published *continuously* since 1802, the *New American Practical Navigator* is now in about its *seventieth edition* and is one of the world's great best sellers of all times. Bowditch and, after his death, his family, carefully amended it and republished it until 1868. At this time the task was taken over by the United States Government —the Hydrographic Office of the Bureau of Navigation, United States Navy. Known officially as H.O. No. 9, it is truly a national monument.

Until the period after World War I and the advent of newer methods (for example, lunar sights are no longer used; accurate chronometers do the work much better), particularly electronic, such as loran, radar, and inertial guidance systems to mention only a few, "The Bowditch" as the book was called, was the navigator's bible. Even today however, the work is still going strong. It is the basic reference and working text on celestial navigation— in the air and on the sea. It will be found in the chart-room of every ship that sails the oceans, in as many languages as there are flags on the sea.

Bowditch never again sailed after the famous voyage of the *Putnam*. As the years passed he emerged from his shell of loneliness. He took an active part—vociferous and, naturally, hot-tempered—part in community affairs such as politics, school elections, and the like. He reared a large and very notable family. He was an expert on insurance matters, particularly in the field of computing risks and developing actuarial tables, and he helped establish the first maritime insurance company in America.

In 1823 he moved to Boston with his family, where he

continued to prosper. His "commentaries" on Laplace's *Mécanique Céleste* ran to four thousand pages, more than twice the size of the original! Bowditch bore the cost—more than $12,000—of publishing this monumental work himself. He also brought out many other works on comets, meteors, and solar eclipses. His greatest work, however, the most useful, was the first one—H.O. 9, "The Bowditch."

Honors were heaped on him. He was made a fellow of the Royal Society of London and of Edinburgh, the Royal Academy of Palermo and Berlin, the Royal Irish Society, the Royal Astronomical Society, and many others. He was elected secretary of the sacrosanct East India Marine Society of Salem and offered various chairs in mathematics and natural philosophy—at Harvard, at the University of Virginia, and at the United States Military Academy at West Point. He was elected President of the American Academy of Arts and Sciences. In 1810 he was elected an overseer at Harvard and in 1826 was made a member of its governing corporation.

When Nat Bowditch died in 1838, ships of all nations in ports throughout the world flew their flags at half-mast as the news spread. Cadets at the United States Naval School at Annapolis wore mourning badges. It was as though sailors everywhere grieved for the loss of a great scientific and mathematical genius, but also, and more importantly for them, they lamented the death of a very good and trustworthy friend whose work guided them safely across dark and trackless oceans.

Possibly, however, the greatest honor, and certainly one that would have pleased most his modest soul, was the inscription on the commemorative statue erected in Salem by the Marine Society: ". . . As long as ships shall sail, the needle point to the North, and stars go through their wonted courses in the heavens, the name of Doctor Bowditch will be revered."

PAUL RINK spent his childhood and boyhood in a small town on Monterey Bay, about 100 miles south of San Francisco. At college his interests were divided between courses in engineering and literature. Out of college, his life has gone along these same lines.

Mr. Rink has traveled extensively. For many years he went to sea, serving as engine-room watch officer on many large vessels.

While living in Latin America, he was in the import-export business, on the staff of the U. S. Embassy in Panama, and worked on a salvage ship for the PanCanal. During this period he was writing in his spare time.

Since 1963, Mr. Rink has been concentrating on writing for magazines, TV, and, of course, books. His hobbies include reading, planning new books, and sailing.